Gill Skills

WORD WIZARD

4TH CLASS

Literacy Skills and Activities

Lorraine Lawrance

g GILL EDUCATION

Contents

How to Use this Book

Comprehension strategies

Having been introduced to all comprehension strategies in *Word Wizard 3rd Class*, in this book pupils are exposed to a variety of engaging activities designed to enhance their comprehension skills before, during and after reading.

 This symbol indicates a comprehension activity to be carried out **before reading**.

 This symbol indicates a comprehension activity to be carried out **during reading**.

 This symbol indicates a comprehension activity to be carried out **after reading**.

Care has been taken to make these activities as general as possible so that they may be applied to other texts such as a class novel.

Some activities are repeated in order to give pupils sufficient practice in important strategies that will help them to use these strategies independently with future texts.

For a detailed explanation of all comprehension strategies, see page vi.

Vocabulary development

STOP! Use your dictionary to find out the meaning of the **bold** words below.

A stop sign appears before each comprehension reading passage, asking pupils to use their dictionary to find out the meaning of the words in bold in the text before reading. This is designed to facilitate the teaching of tricky vocabulary prior to reading the text.

Cloze procedure

A cloze procedure closely linked to the reading passage has been included in each unit. In the first five units, the missing words are provided in a word box. In subsequent units, the answers can be found on pages 113–114. This allows for much needed practice, helps with confidence-building and develops familiarity with cloze procedures.

Dictation

Two dictation sentences are provided for each unit, incorporating the phonics and grammar taught. Suggestions are provided for extension activities or further revision of grammar.

Assessment

Self-assessment tools are presented following grammar and dictation.

 I can do this!   I'm getting there.    I need help!

Two units dedicated to revision and assessment are provided at the end of the second and third terms. Each includes a special four-day section designed to prompt meaningful revision of phonics and grammar before assessment begins.

Extra

Each unit concludes with a suggested activity for extension work that facilitates integration within the areas of art, debate, drama and others.

Genre writing approach

The series takes a unique approach to genre writing. At this level, genre writing follows a four-week approach, with a fortnight spent on each unit. Two units are dedicated to each genre.

> Discrete oral language activities act as building blocks for genre writing.

> The second unit dedicated to each genre introduces the **language and grammar** that pupils are expected to include in the genre. They are then asked to **edit and rewrite** the piece of writing drafted in the previous unit.

> The first unit dedicated to each genre explores the **structure** of the genre. Pupils are asked to **plan and draft** a piece of writing, usually linked to the comprehension topic.

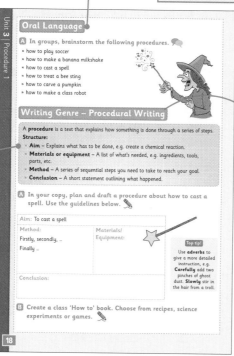

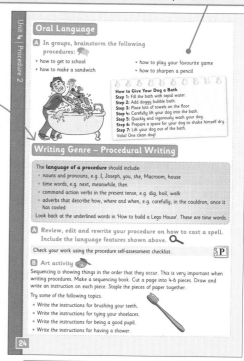

> Grammar activities are linked to the genre wherever appropriate.

> The reading passage serves as a template for the genre. The teacher can refer to this while outlining the structure of the genre, simply through discussion, or by having pupils highlight or underline the various elements.

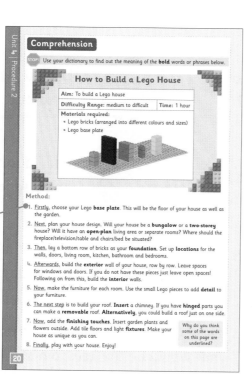

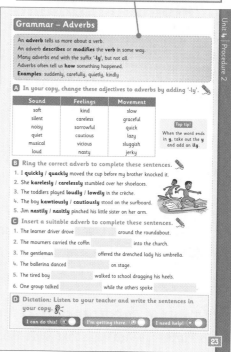

Online resources to support genre writing

- Editable writing frames are provided online to allow pupils to publish their work for an audience.
- Self-assessment checklists are also provided to help pupils edit and self-assess their work.

Comprehension Strategies Guide

Predicting (P) means guessing what will happen. By looking at what has happened in the story already, you can make informed predictions about what might happen next. A book's cover, title, blurb, chapter titles and images also provide clues to help you.

Making Connections (MC) means linking information in the text to something in your own life (text to self), something that you read somewhere else (text to text) or something that you heard about on the television or the radio or from another person (text to world).

Visualising (V) means creating mental pictures based on the text and images.

Questioning (Q): I wonder… This involves asking questions about what you are reading while you read. Keep your mind active and dig deeper into the text.

Word Attack (WA): When you get stuck on a word, use the following bank of Word Attack skills to help you figure it out:

'weather' we, wet, the, her, he, eat, tea, heat	Look for a smaller word in the word.	al-li-ga-tor	Sound out the word. Break it up. Chunk it.
l a ke b oa t d r ea m	Look at the beginning, middle and end of the word.	Prefix Root Suffix	Do you recognise any prefixes, suffixes or root words?
	Look at the images. Is there a clue?	SKIP IT!	Skip the word and read the sentence to the end.
? ?	Make a guess. What would make sense?	Context	Use the words around it. Put it in context.
	Go back and re-read.	or	Use your background knowledge.
DICTIONARY	Use your dictionary or thesaurus.		Picture the word in your mind. What do you see?

Determining Importance (DI) means deciding what is relevant or irrelevant. If you were to tell a stranger what the text was about, what would be the key points?

Inferring (I) means reading between the lines.

Clarifying (C) means figuring out a word, a phrase or an idea that you don't understand. Don't give up! Re-read the text or ask for help to understand it more clearly.

Summarising (S) means choosing the key points from the text.

Homegrown

Top tip!
Look at the Comprehension Strategies Overview Guide on page vi to revise each strategy.

1

Comprehension Strategies

A Before reading: Picture this!

Use the strategy of **Visualising**. The following letter is about Green Schools. What mental image do you have when you hear those words?

B During reading: Fabulous five

Use the strategy of **Determining Importance**. While reading, record five key words in the text. Then, in groups, compare your 'fabulous five' and say why you thought these were the most important words in the text.

C During reading: This reminds me of ...

Use the strategy of **Making Connections**. While reading, stop along the way to make connections to:

- yourself – This reminds me of a time I …
- another text – This reminds me of something I read …
- the outside world – This reminds me of what I know about …

D After reading: Figure it out!

Use the strategies of **Predicting** and **Inferring** to answer these questions.

1. What will the school's reaction be to winning the prize?

2. How will the school decide who gets the iPads?

3. Which class should go to visit the company? What will they do there?

Comprehension

 STOP! Use your dictionary to find out the meaning of the **bold** words and phrases below.

Homegrown

Homegrown Ltd,
Laburnum House,
Grangebeg,
County Waterford

> **Top tip!**
> Ltd is short for 'limited' and is often seen after a company's name.

6 February 2017

Scoil Mhuire Gan Smal,
Timoleague,
County Cork

Dear Principal,

I am writing to **inform** you that your school has won first prize in the Green Schools Community Enterprise Competition. This is a major **achievement**. On **behalf of** the team here at Homegrown, I would like to extend a big congratulations to all involved.

As you know, Homegrown is an eco-company that was set up to **promote** environmental awareness. Choosing a winner was a very hard decision but here is why your school came out on top:

1. The oral presentation given by your 5th Class pupils was highly **commendable** and raised some very interesting points.

2. The parents' and grandparents' involvement in the community clean-up operation was very impressive and it was wonderful to see **generations** of community members getting involved.

3. The standard of care given to the school environment was **second to none**.

4. The written projects undertaken by the 4th Class pupils were carefully planned and each project had something different to offer.

5. The **dedication** of the pupils, teachers and community members of the school was remarkable.

For these reasons, we are delighted to crown Scoil Mhuire Gan Smal our winner. We hope you will enjoy the prize we have in store for you. The prize includes a €2,000 voucher to spend at your local garden centre, six iPads for your school with in-built 'green' apps, a goody bag for every pupil and an all-expenses paid trip for one class to come and visit our company.

Congratulations again and enjoy your well-earned prize.

Yours sincerely,

Harold Turner

Public Relations Manager

A In your copy, go investigate.

1. What is the name of the school that won the prize?
2. Name the company that ran the competition.
3. How did parents and grandparents help?
4. Which class submitted written projects? Why were they so good?
5. What prizes did the school win?

B In your copy, give your opinion.

1. Why did Homegrown run this competition?
2. Why did schools all over the country enter?
3. What do you think impressed Homegrown the most?
4. What do you think in-built 'green' apps are?
5. What do you think the public relations manager's job involves?

C Vocabulary: Match each word with its meaning.

| pollution | climate | carbon dioxide | renew | reusable |

1. Can be used again
2. Contaminating the environment
3. Weather conditions
4. To make like new again
5. The gas we breathe out

D Cloze procedure: 'The Future is Green!' Fill in the blanks.

| plan | Schools | Education | Ireland | habits | Green | seven |

The Department of _____ predicts that by 2020 all schools in _____ will be Green Schools. There are _____ steps involved in becoming a Green School. **1.** A Green _____ Committee **2.** An environmental review **3.** An action _____ **4.** Monitor and evaluate progress **5.** Curriculum work **6.** Keep informing and involving the school and wider community **7.** A _____ Code to show the school's commitment to environmental good _____.

Phonics – 'anti-'

'**anti-**' is a prefix. It comes at the beginning of a word. It means 'against' or 'the opposite of'.

Example: **anti**clockwise. The root word is the main part of the word, i.e. **clockwise**. Anticlockwise means to move in the **opposite** direction to the way in which the hands of a clock move.

A Choose eight words from the list below. Complete the table by breaking each word into its prefix and root.

antibacterial	antisocial	antibiotic	antioxidant
antidandruff	antiseptic	anticyclone	anti-smoking
antifungal	antiperspirant	antiwrinkle	anti-aircraft

Prefix	Root	Prefix	Root
1.		2.	
3.		4.	
5.		6.	
7.		8.	

B Draw a picture to illustrate each word below.

antibiotic	antiwrinkle	anti-smoking

C Use 'anti' words from the table to complete these sentences. Use your dictionary to help you.

1. The police were called because of the _____ behaviour.

2. I needed an _____ ointment for my toe.

3. My mum spent a lot of money on _____ cream.

4. I use _____ gel when I enter and leave a hospital.

5. The weather forecaster said that an _____ is coming in.

Grammar – Punctuation

A Match each word to its meaning and then to its symbol.

1. A dot at the end of a sentence	▪ comma	!
2. To show surprise or excitement	▪ question mark	H
3. Used to ask a question	▪ capital letter	?
4. When someone is talking	▪ exclamation mark	,
5. Used at the beginning of a sentence	▪ full stop	" "
6. Take a breath	▪ speech marks	.

B In your copy, rewrite these sentences using the correct punctuation.

1. there was a gigantic spider in the bath screamed orla
2. is that your hurley and sliotar asked donnacha
3. where is the class going for their music excursion
4. that is the last time I bring you out for a treat declared mum
5. what naughty sheep said little bo peep

C In your copy, rewrite this passage using the correct punctuation.

on sunday 26 of june something terrible happened i was lying in bed and i woke up with a fright and shot out of the bed in a frenzy i made my way downstairs my head was spinning and I felt like i was going to be sick i wondered what my sister would say when she found out how did this happen why did this happen it took a while to gather my thoughts before i rang her to tell her the news my hands were trembling and i felt like i couldn't breathe then somehow i managed to get dressed and made my way to the car

D Dictation: Listen to your teacher and write the sentences in your copy.

I can do this! | I'm getting there. | I need help!

Oral Language

A You can't send that!

The following letter is poorly written. In pairs, discuss the reasons why and suggest how you could improve it.

> To the head guy,
>
> I wanna tell you you won the comp. well done and enjoy the prize. Ye won cos ye were very good at stuff. Fair play.
>
> Harry.

Writing Genre – To Socialise

Letter writing is a form of writing to socialise. There is a certain way to write letters which includes:

- **Orientation** – reason for writing
- **Body** – what do you want to say?
- **Prompt** – how will you end it?
- Include a **greeting** and a **farewell**

A In your copy, plan and draft a letter to your school about a competition your class is invited to enter, e.g. a science competition to create a volcano or a PE competition to become an Active School. Use the guidelines below.

1. **Address** (school's address)
2. **Date**
3. **Address** (your address)
4. **Greeting**
5. **Orientation/Body of letter/Prompt**
6. **Farewell**

B Art activity

Design a poster highlighting your school as a Green School.

Eddie's Party Invitation 2

Comprehension Strategies

A Before reading: Picture this!

Use the strategy of **Visualising**. Look at the words in the box and draw an image to show what you can picture.

party	wish
celebrate	birthday
presents	invitation
friends	age
cake	candle

B Before reading: That reminds me...

Use the strategy of **Making Connections**. Can you make a connection to **(a)** one of your own birthday parties **(b)** a party you have been to **(c)** a party you would like to go to? Fill in the cupcakes with your connections.

(a)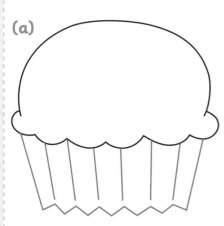

(b)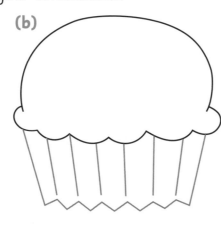

(c)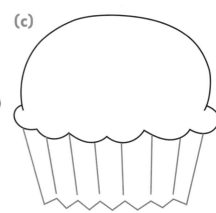

C After reading: What do you think?

Use the strategy of **Inferring**. Write three things that you think happened at Eddie's party.

1. _____

2. _____

3. _____

Comprehension

 STOP! Use your dictionary to find out the meaning of the **bold** words below.

Eddie's Party Invitation

Hooray it's Eddie's Birthday!

Dear Tom,

You are **cordially** invited to celebrate Eddie's 10th birthday. The party will take place on Thursday 2 March at 2pm.

The **venue** for the party is FlyHigh which is located on the **outskirts** of Westport. FlyHigh is an indoor trampoline **arena**, the first of its kind in **Connacht**! It **features** wall-to-wall trampolines with a **variety** of action-packed **zones** including open foam **pits** that kids can jump into, a **dodgeball** zone and a 'dunk zone' for basketball. It is an **adrenaline** buzz from start to finish!

Following these fun activities, you will be **escorted** to the dining lab where you will enjoy an assortment of hot and cold foods. Please let us know if you have any special **dietary** requirements.

We look forward to seeing you on Eddie's special day. Please wear **comfortable** clothes to the party. You can purchase FlyHigh socks at the counter for €1.

_____

RSVP

I <u>will</u> / <u>will not</u> be able to attend Eddie's birthday party.

(Please let us know as soon as possible.)

A **In your copy, go investigate.**

1. Where and when is Eddie's party taking place?
2. What is FlyHigh?
3. Name three activities you can do at FlyHigh.
4. Where will the guests dine?
5. How much do FlyHigh socks cost?

B **In your copy, give your opinion.**

1. Why do you think Eddie has chosen FlyHigh for his party?
2. Will everybody like the activities? Why/Why not?
3. What kind of dietary requirements would some people have?
4. Name some foods that you think will be served at the party.
5. Why is it important to RSVP to an invitation?

> **Top tip!**
>
> RSVP is a French term, *répondez, s'il vous plaît*, meaning please reply.

C **Vocabulary**

In your copy, write antonyms (opposites) from the text for the following words.

1. unfriendly
2. night
3. boring
4. cold
5. uncomfortable
6. closed
7. outdoor
8. finish
9. sell
10. last

D **Cloze procedure: 'Trampolines'. Fill in the blanks.**

> Olympic   diving   piece   decade   stretched   fun   countries

A trampoline is a device made up of a _____ of strong fabric _____ over a steel frame using lots of coiled springs. The name comes from the Spanish *'trampolín'*, meaning a _____ board. A gymnast named George Nissen built the first modern trampoline in his garage in 1936. People bounce on trampolines for _____ and for competitions. Trampolining became an _____ sport in 2000. Many _____ have started developing trampolining programmes. China's trampolining programme developed world-champion athletes in less than a _____ !

Phonics – '-ically'

'**-ically**' is a suffix. It comes at the end of a word and makes an adverb with the meaning of the root word.

Example: alphabet**ically** – 'alphabet' is the root word and the adverb is 'alphabetically'. 'Alphabet' means a series of letters. 'Alphabetically' tells us how the letters are arranged.

A Write the root word for each of the following words.

Word	Root word	Word	Root word
1. artistically		2. robotically	
3. politically		4. vertically	
5. typically		6. alphabetically	
7. historically		8. romantically	
9. majestically		10. rhythmically	
11. melodically		12. critically	

B Write a suitable '-ically' word from the table below each picture.

C Fill in the blanks using a suitable '-ically' word from the table.

1. Martina played the drum _____ in the concert.

2. The curtain rail should not be hung _____.

3. The politician made a statement that was _____ incorrect.

4. The king and queen walked _____ through the palace.

5. He proposed _____ on the beach with a song he wrote for her.

Grammar – Nouns

A **noun** is a person, a place, an animal or a thing. It is a naming word. A **proper noun** is a special word or name that we use for a person, a place or an organisation, e.g. Conor, Italy, Ferrari. A **common noun** names non-specific people, places, things or ideas, e.g. girl, cat, church.

A Sort these proper nouns and common nouns into the correct boxes.

aeroplane	suitcase	Michael	book	apple
Wexford	website	toy	lizard	Spider-Man
clock	Clare	Lego	baby	tulip
Áras an Uachtaráin	butterfly	Paris	banana	cousin

Proper Noun	Common Noun

B In your copy, list the nouns that you can see in this picture.

Jymbo's Super Circus
Punchestown

C Dictation: Listen to your teacher and write the sentences in your copy.

I can do this!   I'm getting there. ○ I need help!

Oral Language

A Thinking outside the box

In pairs, discuss the invitations the following would send out for their birthday parties.

- a baby
- a chef
- an Olympic athlete
- a teenager
- a magician
- an astronaut

Writing Genre – To Socialise

The purpose of a **text used to socialise** is to maintain or improve relationships or to send a message from the sender to the recipient. A socialising text may be formal or informal.

The **language of texts used to socialise** should include:

- pronouns – I, you, we
- specific subjects or people – Aunty Grace, Mr Lawrence
- questions – How are you? Is Millie feeling better?
- simple past tense
- action verbs – designed, visited
- words to show time – then, next week

A Review, edit and rewrite the letter to your school about the competition they are invited to enter. Include the language features shown above.

Check your work using the to socialise self-assessment checklist. **P**

B In your copy, write an invitation to your friends inviting them to your birthday party. ✏

C Art activity 🎨

Design an invitation for an aquatic-themed birthday party. Include details about the party.

- Whose party is it?
- Who is invited?
- Where is it on?
- When is it on?

Volcanic Experiment

Comprehension Strategies

A Before reading: Guess the science

Use the strategy of **Predicting**. What do you predict will happen when baking soda and vinegar are mixed?

B During reading: Picture this!

Use the strategy of **Visualising**. Draw an image of what you think might happen in some key steps of the process.

Step 1	Step 2	Step 3	Step 4

C After reading: Figure it out!

Use the strategies of **Predicting** and **Inferring** to answer these questions.

1. What do you think would happen if you changed the amount of baking soda or vinegar?

   _____

2. What might happen if you used other acids instead of vinegar or other bases instead of baking soda? Examples of acids include lemon juice or ketchup. Examples of bases include laundry detergent or household ammonia.

   _____

   _____

   _____

   _____

   _____

Comprehension

STOP! Use your dictionary to find out the meaning of the **bold** words and phrases below.

Volcanic Experiment

Aim: To see if mixing baking soda and vinegar creates a **chemical reaction**.	
Difficulty Range: Average	**Time:** 30 minutes
Materials required: ■ $\frac{1}{4}$ cup vinegar ■ 2 tablespoons baking soda ■ Warm water ■ Dishwashing **detergent** ■ Red food colouring	**Equipment:** ■ Plastic bottle ■ Baking tray ■ Kitchen paper ■ A cool, dark place

Method:

1. Make a volcano out of **papier mâché** or Play-Doh. You could also use a mound of clay and do your experiment outside.

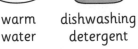

warm water dishwashing detergent food colouring

2. Stand the plastic bottle in the volcano and place the volcano on the baking tray. Remove the top of the bottle.

3. Fill the bottle most of the way with warm water and add a few drops of red food colouring.

4. Squeeze six drops of detergent into the bottle. The detergent helps trap the bubbles that are made by the **reaction** so you will get better **lava**.

5. Add two tablespoons of baking soda to the bottle.

6. Then, slowly pour the vinegar into the bottle.

7. **Observe** what happens.

Top tip!

What is happening? The red lava is the result of a **chemical reaction** between the baking soda and the vinegar. In this reaction, carbon dioxide gas is produced. Pressure builds up inside the plastic bottle until the gas bubbles out of the top.

Result:

A volcanic explosion! The mixture **rapidly** fizzes over.

Conclusion:

When you mix baking soda and vinegar they react together.

A In your copy, go investigate.

1. What is the aim of the experiment?
2. Name five items that you will need to carry out this task.
3. What is the first thing you have to do?
4. When do you add the food colouring?
5. What happens when the vinegar is added to the bottle?

B In your copy, give your opinion.

1. Is the volcano easy to make? What other material could you use?
2. Why do you need to use a plastic bottle?
3. What is the function of the food colouring?
4. How do you know how much vinegar to pour in?
5. Is this a safe experiment? Why/Why not?

C Vocabulary

Use this word list and your dictionary or encyclopaedia to find out more about volcanoes.

active volcano	ash	ash cloud	core	crater	crust
dormant volcano	eruption	extinct volcano	fault	hot spot	lava

D Cloze procedure: 'The Buried Town'. Fill in the blanks.

remains	southern	killed	buried	streets	tourists	eruption	time

Pompeii was a Roman town in _____ Italy. On 24 August 79AD, Pompeii was _____ under volcanic ash and rock following the _____ of the volcano, Mount Vesuvius. Most of the people in the town were _____ . Pompeii was excavated 1,600 years later and the _____ of many items, buildings and people were found in a 'petrified' state. This means that they stayed the same as they were at the _____ of the eruption. Thousands of _____ visit Pompeii every year to walk through the _____ of what was once a busy town.

15

Phonics – Homophones

Homophones are words that sound alike but have different meanings and different spellings.

Examples:

The **deer** lives in the forest.
Dear Eilish, how are you?

This is the **way** to my house.
I must **weigh** the flour for the recipe.

There are **eight** players on the team.
I **ate** an apple for my snack.

I would love to eat a juicy **pear**.
A **pair** of shoes was left on the bus.

A Ring the correct homophone.

1. My sister likes to **die / dye** her hair blonde.

2. Please don't **waste / waist** the paper.

3. Prince Charles is the **heir / air** to the British throne.

4. My favourite dinner is **stake / steak** and chips.

5. I would love to eat a **piece / peace** of that cake.

B In your copy, rewrite this poem using the correct homophones.

Eye halve a spelling chequer

It came with my pea sea

It plainly marques four my revue

Miss steaks eye kin knot sea.

Eye strike a quay and type a word

And weight four it two say

Weather eye am wrong oar write

It shows me strait a weigh.

As soon as a mist ache is maid

It nose bee fore two long

And eye can put the error rite

It's rare lea ever wrong.

Eye have run this poem threw it

I am shore your pleased two no

It's letter perfect awl the weigh

My chequer tolled me sew.

(Sauce Unknown)

C In your copy, make a list of homophones. Write sentences using both words.

Example: The **knight** galloped through the woods at **night**.

Grammar – Verbs

A **verb** is a word that tells what the noun is doing. It is an action word.

Example: The girl is **reading**. The action that the girl is doing is reading.

A Underline the verb in each sentence.

1. The vulture captured its prey.
2. The doctor found a cure for the disease.
3. Hansel escaped from the cage.
4. The thieves stole the treasure from the island.
5. The artist sketched a funny caricature.

The **present** tense tells us what is happening now.

Example: I **am eating** the apple.

The **past** tense tells us something that already happened.

Example: I **ate** the apple.

The **future** tense tells us something that will happen later.

Example: I **will eat** the apple soon.

B Complete the table of present, past and future verbs.

	Present	Past	Future
blow	I blow	I blew	I will blow
tap			
shake			
dance			

C In your copy, write an interesting paragraph using these verbs.

climb   dash   gallop   leap   race   skid   prance   trot   trudge

D Dictation: Listen to your teacher and write the sentences in your copy.

 I can do this!   I'm getting there.   I need help!

17

Oral Language

A In groups, brainstorm the following procedures.

- how to play soccer
- how to make a banana milkshake
- how to cast a spell
- how to treat a bee sting
- how to carve a pumpkin
- how to make a class robot

Writing Genre – Procedural Writing

A **procedure** is a text that explains how something is done through a series of steps.

Structure:

- **Aim** – Explains what has to be done, e.g. create a chemical reaction.
- **Materials or equipment** – A list of what's needed, e.g. ingredients, tools, parts, etc.
- **Method** – A series of sequential steps you need to take to reach your goal.
- **Conclusion** – A short statement outlining what happened.

A In your copy, plan and draft a procedure about how to cast a spell. Use the guidelines below.

Aim: To cast a spell	
Method: Firstly, secondly, … Finally …	**Materials/ Equipment:**
Conclusion:	

Top tip!

Use **adverbs** to give a more detailed instruction, e.g. **Carefully** add two pinches of ghost dust. **Slowly** stir in the hair from a troll.

B Create a class 'How to' book. Choose from recipes, science experiments or games.

How to Build a Lego House

4

Comprehension Strategies

A Before reading: Picture this!

Use the strategy of **Visualising**. Draw a design of your dream house. Think of colour, layout and size.

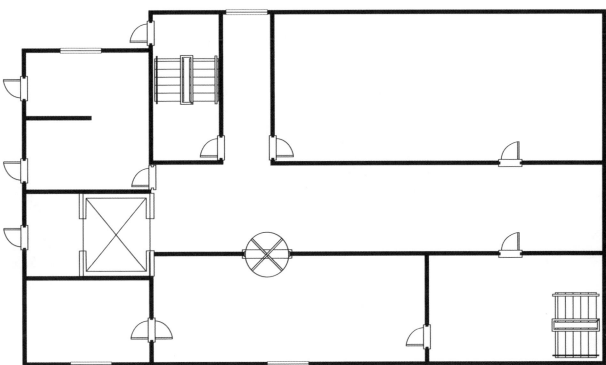

B During reading: Spring cleaning!

Use the strategy of **Determining Importance**. Decide which items are essential or non-essential for your Lego house.

Essential items	Non-essential items
1.	1.
2.	2.
3.	3.
4.	4.
5.	5.

C After reading: What did you do?

Use the strategy of **Summarising**. In pairs, explain to your partner the procedure you followed to make your Lego house.

Comprehension

STOP! Use your dictionary to find out the meaning of the **bold** words or phrases below.

How to Build a Lego House

Aim: To build a Lego house	
Difficulty Range: medium to difficult	**Time:** 1 hour

Materials required:
- Lego bricks (arranged into different colours and sizes)
- Lego base plate

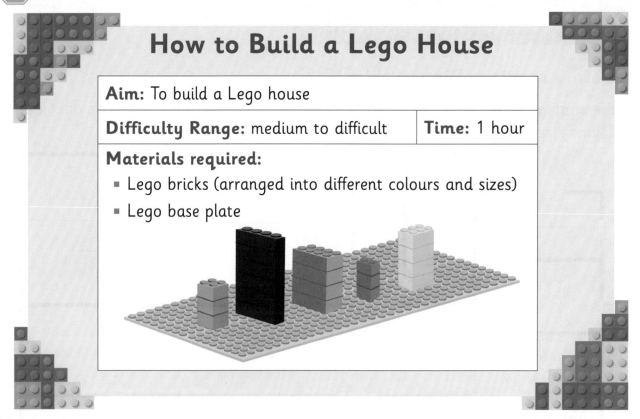

Method:

1. <u>Firstly</u>, choose your Lego **base plate**. This will be the floor of your house as well as the garden.

2. <u>Next</u>, plan your house design. Will your house be a **bungalow** or a **two-storey** house? Will it have an **open-plan** living area or separate rooms? Where should the fireplace/television/table and chairs/bed be situated?

3. <u>Then</u>, lay a bottom row of bricks as your **foundation**. Set up **locations** for the walls, doors, living room, kitchen, bathroom and bedrooms.

4. <u>Afterwards</u>, build the **exterior** wall of your house, row by row. Leave spaces for windows and doors. If you do not have these pieces just leave open spaces! Following on from this, build the **interior** walls.

5. <u>Now</u>, make the furniture for each room. Use the small Lego pieces to add **detail** to your furniture.

6. <u>The next step</u> is to build your roof. **Insert** a chimney. If you have **hinged** parts you can make a **removable** roof. **Alternatively**, you could build a roof just on one side.

7. <u>Now</u>, add the **finishing touches**. Insert garden plants and flowers outside. Add tile floors and light **fixtures**. Make your house as unique as you can.

> Why do you think some of the words on this page are underlined?

8. <u>Finally</u>, play with your house. Enjoy!

A In your copy, go investigate.

1. What item do you need to build your house upon?
2. What is the bottom row of bricks called?
3. What must you leave space for when building the exterior walls?
4. What Lego pieces could you use for a removable roof?
5. Describe what the finishing touches might be.

B In your copy, give your opinion.

1. Why is it important to plan your house design?
2. What are the benefits of open-plan living as against separate living spaces? What would not be good about open-plan living?
3. Why does a house need a chimney?
4. Why would a hinged roof be a good idea?
5. Would you like to be an architect? What skills would you need?

C Vocabulary

Using the words below, write descriptive sentences about houses, e.g. The crumbling hovel was painted stony-grey and had a ghostly feeling when you reached the staircase.

Size	Texture	Colour	Attributes	Objects
enormous	dusty	olive-green	eerie	doors
poky	mossy	frosty-blue	cheerful	roof
compact	bare	blood-red	ancient	windows
large	rough	snowy-white	cosy	arches
tiny	cob-webbed	coal-black	silent	walls

D Cloze procedure: 'Crowded House'. Fill in the blanks.

| crowded | kitchen | living | terraced | television | much | stories |

My great-grandfather lived in a _____ house in the early 1900s. It was a two-bed house with a _____ , a small living room and a toilet. It was damp, cold and dilapidated. There were ten people _____ in the house. Disease was rampant in the _____ conditions. There was no _____ or electricity. They played cards and told _____ to pass the time. The children were happy with what they had, even though they did not have _____ .

21

Phonics – '-qu'

q and u come together to make the 'qu' sound. It sounds like 'kew'.

quiet	squirrel	squash	earthquake	conquest	aquarium
equipment	liquid	squeak	banquet	request	equator
queen	quiz	squid	question	square	quarter
quilt	quack	quality	quit	quote	squirt

A Write a suitable '-qu' word from the table below each picture.

_____   _____   _____   _____

_____   _____   _____   _____

B Match a '-qu' word from the table with a definition below.

1. A feast _____

2. The sound a mouse makes _____

3. To give up _____

4. To ask for something _____

5. A blanket for your bed _____

6. A place where you can go and see fish _____

7. The opposite of loud _____

8. A shape with four corners _____

C In your copy, choose six words from the table of '-qu' words and write a sentence for each. Draw an image to show the key word in each sentence.

Example: The king ordered a **banquet** to celebrate his victory.

Grammar – Adverbs

An **adverb** tells us more about a verb.

An adverb **describes** or **modifies** the **verb** in some way.

Many adverbs end with the suffix '**-ly**', but not all.

Adverbs often tell us **how** something happened.

Examples: suddenly, carefully, quietly, kindly

A In your copy, change these adjectives to adverbs by adding '-ly'.

Sound	Feelings	Movement
soft	kind	slow
silent	careless	graceful
noisy	sorrowful	quick
quiet	cautious	lazy
musical	vicious	sluggish
loud	nasty	jerky

Top tip!

When the word ends in **y**, take out the **y** and add an **ily**.

B Ring the correct adverb to complete these sentences.

1. I **quickly** / **quackly** moved the cup before my brother knocked it.

2. She **karelesly** / **carelessly** stumbled over her shoelaces.

3. The toddlers played **loudly** / **lowdly** in the crèche.

4. The boy **kawtiously** / **cautiously** stood on the surfboard.

5. Jim **nastily** / **nasitly** pinched his little sister on her arm.

C Insert a suitable adverb to complete these sentences.

1. The learner driver drove _____ around the roundabout.

2. The mourners carried the coffin _____ into the church.

3. The gentleman _____ offered the drenched lady his umbrella.

4. The ballerina danced _____ on stage.

5. The tired boy _____ walked to school dragging his heels.

6. One group talked _____ while the others spoke _____.

D Dictation: Listen to your teacher and write the sentences in your copy.

I can do this!   I'm getting there.   I need help!

Oral Language

A **In groups, brainstorm the following procedures:**

- how to get to school
- how to make a sandwich

- how to play your favourite game
- how to sharpen a pencil

How to Give Your Dog a Bath
Step 1: Fill the bath with tepid water.
Step 2: Add doggy bubble bath.
Step 3: Place lots of towels on the floor.
Step 4: Carefully lift your dog into the bath.
Step 5: Quickly and vigorously wash your dog.
Step 6: Prepare a space for your dog to shake himself dry.
Step 7: Lift your dog out of the bath.
Voila! One clean dog!

Writing Genre – Procedural Writing

The **language of a procedure** should include:

- nouns and pronouns, e.g. I, Joseph, you, she, Macroom, house
- time words, e.g. next, meanwhile, then
- command action verbs in the present tense, e.g. dig, boil, walk
- adverbs that describe how, where and when, e.g. carefully, in the cauldron, once it has cooled

Look back at the underlined words in 'How to build a Lego House'. These are time words.

A **Review, edit and rewrite your procedure on how to cast a spell. Include the language features shown above.**

Check your work using the procedure self-assessment checklist.

B **Art activity**

Sequencing is showing things in the order that they occur. This is very important when writing procedures. Make a sequencing book. Cut a page into 4-6 pieces. Draw and write an instruction on each piece. Staple the pieces of paper together.

Try some of the following topics.

- Write the instructions for brushing your teeth.
- Write the instructions for tying your shoelaces.
- Write the instructions for being a good pupil.
- Write the instructions for having a shower.

Gulliver in the Land of Lilliput 5

Comprehension Strategies

A Before reading: Crystal ball

Use the strategy of **Predicting**. Look at the title and image and use your crystal ball to predict what the story will be about.

I predict that…   I imagine that…   I wonder if…   I think that…

I think that … will happen, because…   Maybe… will happen, because…

B During reading: This reminds me of …

Use the strategy of **Making Connections**. While reading, stop along the way to make connections to:

- yourself – This reminds me of a time I …
- another text – This reminds me of something I read …
- the outside world – This reminds me of what I know about …

C During reading: Picture this! …

Use the strategy of **Visualising**. Draw a picture to match the following image from the text.

'… the sea was black, the waves were huge, and the mast was creaking fit to snap off.'

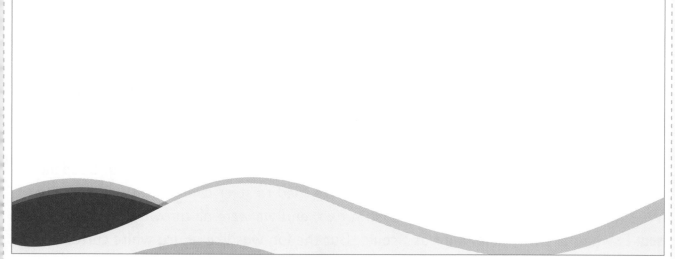

D After reading: Main points

Use the strategy of **Determining Importance**. Decide what you think is the main point in each paragraph. In groups, see if everyone agrees with your choice.

Comprehension

 Use your dictionary to find out the meaning of the **bold** words and phrases below.

Gulliver in the Land of Lilliput

My name is Gulliver, and I have a **tale** to tell that will make your hair stand up and your mouth hang open. All I ever wanted was to travel and have amazing adventures. So one spring day, I threw some clothes into a bag, said goodbye to my shocked family, and **boarded** the *Antelope*, a ship **bound** for the Tropics.

We sailed east into the **rising** sun. My work was not hard. There was plenty to eat, and the other lads were **lively**. When we stopped for food or water, there were exciting places to visit. I was having a wonderful time. But one night, all this changed …

"Bad weather coming," said the captain **grimly**. In no time, the sea was black, the waves were huge, and the **mast** was **creaking** fit to snap off. The **gale** hit us like a **massive** hammer. The crew worked hard, but by the time the **wind died down**, we were lost. Much as I loved adventure, *this* was not what I'd had in mind. But worse was yet to come.

A **dense**, ghostly fog floated down, and we couldn't see where we were going. Suddenly, looming out of nowhere, was a massive rock! We tried to steer away but it was too late. We smashed straight into it, the ship split in two, and we were all thrown into the freezing sea. I swam for the rock as hard as I could. But the fog was like an icy white curtain, and I could see nothing. "Help!" I shouted, but there was no answer. I was all alone. I swam and swam until my arms and legs were like burning lumps of **lead**. Just as I was about to give up and drown, my foot touched something **solid** beneath me. It was sand – I was saved!

(From '*Gulliver*' retold by Mary Webb)

A In your copy, go investigate.

1. What two things did Gulliver say this tale will make you do?
2. What was it that Gulliver always wanted to do?
3. Name the three things Gulliver did before he went to the Tropics.
4. What came looming out of nowhere? What happened next?
5. What did Gulliver's foot touch?

B In your copy, give your opinion.

1. Why do you think Gulliver's family were shocked?
2. Describe what life was like on board the ship.
3. How did everything change one night?
4. What is meant by the 'gale hit us like a massive hammer'?
5. What happened after the storm? What do you think will happen next?

C Vocabulary

In pairs, discuss what these phrases from the text mean. Illustrate them in the boxes below.

Hair stand up	Mouth hang open	Dense ghostly fog	Burning lumps of lead

D Cloze procedure: 'Gulliver's Travels'. Fill in the blanks.

> cultures   tiny   adventures   English   giant
> Jonathan   sails   shipwrecked   people

'Gulliver's Travels' was written by an Irish writer named _____ Swift in 1726. It is one of the most popular books ever written in the _____ language. The book tells the story of Gulliver who _____ around the world and has many _____. He gets _____ and meets the Lilliputians who are _____ people only 50 centimetres tall. On another trip he meets a _____ who is 23 metres tall. Although the book is about Gulliver, the author also wants to teach us that all _____ are different and the world is full of different _____.

Phonics – '-nch'

Examples:

stench	punch	pinch	hunchback	launch	branch
crunch	enchantment	bench	scrunch	French	inch
anchor	munch	franchise	wrench	flinch	Lynch
lunch	drench	trench	finch	bunch	ranch

A Match an '-nch' word from the table with a definition below.

1. The language spoken in France

2. A measure equal to 2.5 cm

3. A heavy object used to make a boat stay in one place

4. A part of a tree that grows out from the trunk

5. A strong and very unpleasant smell

6. A breaking or crushing noise

B Ring the correct '-nch' word to complete these sentences.

1. There was a **stench / crunch** from the rotting fish.
2. There was a **French / branch** in the overgrown garden.
3. He sat on a **bench / launch** on the enchanted island.
4. Alice **franchise / pinched** Alex when her mother was not looking.
5. Mr **scrunch / Lynch** lived near Onslow Gardens.
6. The boxer tried to **munch / punch** the referee by mistake.

C Insert a suitable '-nch' word from the table to complete these sentences.

1. The entire class were invited to the   of the author's new book.

2. Bonjour is the   word for hello.

3. McDonald's is a   that is located all over the world.

4. I saw the '   of Notre Dame' in the theatre.

5. The fairy trail filled the children with a sense of   .

6. If I   my hair when it is wet, it goes curly.

Grammar – Adjectives

An **adjective** is a word that describes a noun. A noun is a person, a place, a thing, an animal or an event. Adjectives make sentences more interesting.

Example: The **frightened boy** ran out of the haunted house.

Frightened is the **adjective** describing the boy which is the **noun**.

A Make a list of adjectives under each heading in the table.

Colour	Size	Sound	Shape
sky-blue	enormous	deafening	rounded

Weather	Number	Taste	Texture
stormy	few	sweet	rough

B Insert a suitable adjective to complete the sentences.

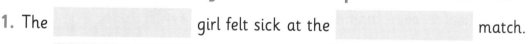

1. The   girl felt sick at the   match.

2. The   boy tripped on a   stone.

3. It was a   day in the   resort.

4. The   boy ate the   strawberries.

5. I won a   medal at the   competition.

C Pick an object and hide it from view. Use adjectives to describe the object. Your partner must guess the object.

D Dictation: Listen to your teacher and write the sentences in your copy.

I can do this!   I'm getting there.   I need help!

Oral Language

A Read the opening sentences below. Use your imagination. In pairs, discuss what you can see, hear, smell, taste and touch.

- One stormy day a very long time ago …
- It all began when Lainey entered the cave …
- In a distant land where only robots exist …
- There was a knock at the door and she was home alone …

Writing Genre – Narrative Writing

A **narrative** is a fictional story written to entertain the reader.

Structure:

- **Orientation** – Introduce the setting, time and main character. Set the mood/tone.
- **Series of events** – An initial event (how did the characters get involved?) and a problem or complication for the main character.
- **Resolution** – The problem is usually resolved for the main character.

The **hook line** in a narrative is a sentence or series of sentences at the beginning that grab the reader's attention. The hook line reels the reader in so that they are hooked on the text and are eager to keep reading.

Example:
I have a **tale** to tell that will make your hair stand up and your mouth hang open.

A As a class, brainstorm hook lines. Keep a record of them for future use.

B In your copy, plan and draft a narrative story in which your main character has been shipwrecked. Don't forget your hook line!

C Drama: Conscience Alley

The class stands in two lines, creating a Conscience Alley. In the role of a shipwrecked child, one pupil walks through Conscience Alley. What would it feel like alone on an island? What would you eat? Who would you talk to? How would you plan to get home? When tapped on the shoulder, the pupil tells the class what she/he is thinking.

Jánošík – A Polish Legend   6

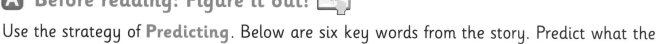

Comprehension Strategies

A Before reading: Figure it out!

Use the strategy of **Predicting**. Below are six key words from the story. Predict what the legend of Jánošík will be about.

| thief | landlord | hungry | hero | witches | escaped |

B Before reading: KWL chart

Use the strategies of **Making Connections** and **Questioning**. Use the chart below to record your background knowledge and anything you hope to find out from reading the text. Record what you have learned after reading.

KWL Chart		
What I know	**What I want to know**	**What I have learned**

C During reading: Stop and think ...

Use the strategy of **Making Connections**.

- Who does Jánošík remind you of?
- Did you ever feel how Jánošík felt when the poor people were unfairly treated?
- What does the moral of the story teach us about the world?

D After reading: Learning new words

Use the strategy of **Word Attack**. (Do you remember how to attack words? Look back to page vi.) Pick out three words from the text. Say which word attack strategy you used to figure them out.

Word _____
W.A.S. _____

Word _____
W.A.S. _____

Word _____
W.A.S. _____

Comprehension

 STOP! Use your dictionary to find out the meaning of the **bold** words below.

Jánošík – A Polish Legend

Long ago, poor starving people living in the Tatra Mountain area of Poland were **charged** unfair rents by greedy landlords. One day, a boy named Jánošík met a rich man climbing a mountain with two of his soldiers. One of the soldiers tried to push Jánošík off the mountain path. Jánošík hit the **bully** and the bully fell off the slope. As the second soldier came to attack him, Jánošík tripped him and he too fell off the mountain.

Then, Jánošík took the rich man's heavy bag, which was full of money the man had collected from the poor people. Jánošík gave the money to poor **starving** families. He had to hide in the mountains because he knew that other soldiers would be looking for him.

As he climbed the mountain, he noticed three witches walking silently behind him. The witches told Jánošík that they had been watching him and that they knew that he had pushed the soldiers off the mountain and had stolen the money. But they saw him give the money to poor families and **considered** him a hero. Each of the witches gave Jánošík a magical gift – the first gift was a woollen shirt that would stop any bullet or arrow, the second gift was a red leather belt that would help him run more swiftly and the third gift was a long-handled mountaineer's axe that would allow Jánošík to climb **steep** cliffs and peaks where no one could follow him.

Jánošík soon became the chief of a group of **bandits** who robbed the rich and gave the stolen treasures to the poor people. He was thought of as a hero by the poor. The landlords offered enormous rewards for his **capture**, but the gifts of the witches made it **impossible** for him to be caught. A woman, who lived in the mountains and knew Jánošík, told the soldiers about the three gifts the witches had given him. One night, the woman stole the gifts and built a fire on the mountainside to **signal** to the soldiers that she had taken them. When the soldiers arrived, Jánošík no longer had his magic powers. He fought **bravely** but was taken to prison. The mean woman ran away. Jánošík escaped from prison and legend has it that to this day he still lives in the mountains robbing from the rich and giving to the poor.

A In your copy, go investigate.

1. Why were the people in the Tatra Mountain area poor?
2. What did Jánošík do one day?
3. Who did Jánošík give the money to? Why?
4. What were the three gifts that the witches gave to Jánošík?
5. How did the woman betray Jánošík?

B In your copy, give your opinion.

1. Why do you think Jánošík wanted to help the poor?
2. How do you think the landlords felt when they charged unfair rents?
3. How did the landlords feel when Jánošík stole from them?
4. Why do you think the witches wanted Jánošík to become a hero?
5. How do you think Jánošík escaped from prison?

C Vocabulary

Write the words in bold from the comprehension on flashcards. In pairs, take turns sticking a word onto your partner's back. One person describes what the word means and the other person has to guess the word.

D Cloze procedure: 'Jánošík's Jumble'. Fill in the blanks.

Complete the cloze and sequence the events by numbering the sentences in the correct order.

☐	The _____ witches gave Jánošík magical _____ to help him become a better robber.
☐	A _____ stole Jánošík's axe, belt, and _____.
☐	The woman made a _____ to signal to the soldiers that she had stolen the gifts.
☐	Jánošík _____ from prison and legend has it that to this day he still robs from the rich and gives to the _____!
☐	Jánošík gave the stolen _____ to poor _____.
1	The people of the _____ Mountains were poor and _____ because greedy landlords charged them unfair rents.

Phonics – '-ure'

'**-ure**' is often seen at the end of a word. It comes from French and Latin words that were taken in to English

Examples: The baby was premat**ure**.

The farmer placed man**ure** in the field.

A In your copy, split the '-ure' words below into their syllables. Clapping out the word as you say it can help with this.

1. vulture	2. insure	3. capture
4. caricature	5. pure	6. cure
7. vulture	8. manure	9. reassure
10. manicure	11. mature	12. secure
13. ensure	14. treasure	15. immature
16. insecure	17. premature	18. measure

B Write the correct '-ure' word below each picture.

C Write a suitable '-ure' word from the table to complete these sentences.

1. The bracelet is made of _____ gold.

2. I went to the beauticians to have a _____.

3. The _____ hovered over the dead mouse.

4. Scientists work hard to find a _____ for diseases.

5. The artist drew a _____ of Ruby when she was in Paris.

6. The bank keeps the gold locked in a _____ safe.

Grammar – Speech Marks

Speech marks (" ") are placed before and after **direct speech** to show exactly what a person has said. The punctuation (comma, full stop, exclamation mark or question mark) is always placed inside the speech marks.

Example: did you really think that she was going to let you get away with that you really are foolish said Pat

"Did you really think that she was going to let you get away with that? You really are foolish!" said Pat.

A Insert speech marks in these sentences.

1. I told him not to feed the dog but he wouldn't listen, barked Dad.

2. The smell from the bin is revolting! spluttered Michael.

3. Do you know the way to the new cinema? asked Kate.

4. I will never go to that barbers again! said the boy with the half-shaved head.

5. I like eating cabbage with pasta, remarked Sandra.

B In your copy, write four sentences that include speech marks.

C In your copy, rewrite these sentences with the correct punctuation to show direct speech.

1. Turn off the air conditioning said Con It's too cold in here

2. I don't know what I want for dinner mumbled Eljay

3. Why didn't you come to the cinema asked Alice

4. Have you done your chores yet asked Mum

5. Did she actually let that tarantula crawl up her arm asked Maryanne

6. I cannot hear you remarked Nan

7. Go away said Matt

8. Where do you keep the cutlery asked Uncle Kieran

D Dictation: Listen to your teacher and write the sentences in your copy.

I can do this! 　　I'm getting there.　　I need help!

Oral Language

A In pairs, take turns to describe in detail what you would do if you had Jánošík's magic gifts.

Writing Genre – Narrative Writing

The **language of a narrative** should include:

- nouns and pronouns that refer to specific characters – Jánošík, witches
- first or third person – I, we
- past tense – robbed, escaped
- action verbs – climbed, push
- descriptive adjectives – starving, greedy
- linking words to show time – then, long ago

A Brainstorming: In pairs, examine the following guiding questions and discuss.

Orientation	Characters
■ What will your first sentence be? ■ What will your setting look like? ■ What words will you use to describe it?	■ Who are the characters? ■ What do they look like? ■ What are their personalities like?

Problem	Story Structure
■ What is the main problem in the story?	■ What will happen first, next, last?

Resolution	
■ How will things work out?	■ How will you end your story?

B Review, edit and rewrite your narrative story about a shipwreck. Ask yourself guiding questions while you rewrite your story to make your piece more interesting.

Check your work using the narrative self-assessment checklist.

C Drama: Role-play

Re-enact the story of Jánošík in groups. **Roles**: Jánošík, landlords, woman, witches, poor people.

Claude Monet

Comprehension Strategies

A Before reading: I wonder ...

Use the strategy of **Questioning**. Look at the painting of the poppy field by Monet and fill in the thought bubbles below.

I wonder
_____
_____

I wonder
_____
_____

I wonder
_____
_____

B During reading: What do you think?

Use the strategy of **Inferring**. As you read, stop along the way to make inferences using evidence from the text and the pictures.

I think Monet was ...

- What inspired Monet's paintings?
- What impression do you get of the artist from looking at his paintings?
- What do you like about his paintings?

C After reading: Picture this!

Use the strategy of **Visualising**. Draw your own image inspired by Monet's paintings.

Comprehension

STOP! Use your dictionary to find out the meaning of the **bold** words below.

'Poppy Field', 1873

Claude Monet 1840–1926

Claude Monet was born on 15 November 1840, in Paris. He loved to draw as a child and he especially enjoyed drawing **caricatures** of people. Around the age of 11, Claude went to a school for the arts and began to use oil paints to paint the outdoors.

Claude, along with some other artists, wanted to **experiment** with art. They wanted to do something different to the **classical** art that the art **critics** in Paris liked. They wanted to capture a moment in time. They organised an exhibition of their art and one critic called it the Exhibition of the Impressionists. The term 'impressionist' was used to suggest that the art was just an **impression** of something and not completed. It was meant as an insult.

'Impression, Sunrise', 1872

One of Monet's works called 'Impression, Sunrise' was a great example of the new style. The lighting gives the viewer the feeling or 'impression' that the sun is just rising. Monet's use of light was **unique**. An interesting fact about this picture is the brightness of the sun. It is the same brightness as the sky. If you turn this picture into a black and white picture, the sun **virtually** disappears.

A In your copy, go investigate.

1. What is the first thing you notice when you look at 'Poppy Field'?

2. How many people can you see in the painting?

3. What is the effect of the large tree on the left? What would the painting be like if it were not there?

4. What kind of day is it? Why is the lady carrying an umbrella?

5. What type of art did the art critics in Paris like?

B In your copy, give your opinion.

1. Why are there flowers on the left of 'Poppy Field' but none on the right?

2. Do you think 'Poppy Field' is a good title? Why?/Why not?

3. What conversation do you think the lady and the girl in the painting are having?

4. Where do you think the people in the painting are going?

5. How does 'Impression, Sunrise' give you the impression that the sun is rising?

C Vocabulary

In pairs, use this vocabulary to describe Monet's painting 'Woman with a Parasol':

foreground	background	centre
bottom-left	bottom-right	top-left
top-right	colour	mood
feeling	layers	light
shade	brushstroke	technique
nature	inspiration	soft

D Cloze procedure: 'Monet the Master'. Fill in the blanks.

Monet was born in _____ . When he was young he liked to draw _____ of people. While at art school he used _____ paints and loved to paint the _____ . Monet and his friends liked to experiment with art. His first big exhibition was nicknamed the Exhibition of the _____ by its critics. Monet's use of light was unique. It can be seen in some of his most famous paintings such as '_____' and '_____'. Monet _____ in 1926.

39

Phonics – '-or'

razor	calculator	senior	mirror	horse	tornado
doctor	forget	error	fortnight	motor	order
Portugal	escalator	north	short	storm	sport
decoration	torch	sword	author	terror	opportunity
score	visitor	comfort	illustrator	snore	Cork

A Unscramble the '-or' words and match them with their meaning.

chrot   seroh   ortalesca   donarot   ronth

1. A violent storm.

2. A light to be carried in the hand.

3. A large four-legged animal.

4. A moving staircase.

5. A point on the compass.

B Insert a suitable '-or' word from the table to complete these sentences.

1. My youngest sister always hangs the first _____ on the Christmas tree.

2. Michael Morpurgo is the _____ of 'The Butterfly Lion'.

3. The rain during the _____ caused a flood.

4. "_____, _____ on the wall", is a famous line from 'Snow White'.

5. Joe was so cosy in his bed that he began to _____.

6. The centre-forward had the _____ to _____ a goal.

C In your copy, choose six '-or' words from the table and write a sentence for each. Draw an image to show the key word in each sentence.

Example: Dad cut his jaw while shaving with a sharp **razor**.

Grammar – Verbs: Simple and Continuous Present

Simple present tense refers to an action that is regular, true or normal, e.g. I **walk**.

Continuous present tense refers to an action that is still happening, e.g. I **am walk**ing. To form the continuous present, insert the irregular verb '**to be**' before the verb and add the present participle (usually '**ing**').

A In your copy, use the table to make sentences with verbs in the continuous present. Choose a number to challenge yourself.

Example: I am going to the park to meet my friends.

I	am	am not	swimming	
He She It	is is is	is not is not is not	whispering singing freezing	
We You They	are are are	are not are not are not	talking baking running	

B Create a verb poem using verbs from the continuous present.

On Monday, _____   On Friday, _____

On Tuesday, _____   On Saturday, _____

On Wednesday, _____   On Sunday, _____

On Thursday, _____

C In your copy, change your poem to either the past continuous or the future continuous.

D Dictation: Listen to your teacher and write the sentences in your copy.

I can do this! 👍 ⚪	I'm getting there. 🤔 ⚪	I need help! 👎 ⚪

41

Oral Language

A Working in pairs, choose one of the senses and see what words come into your head for each of these topics: winter, school, holidays, love. Do this for each sense. Compare your words with your partner's words.

Writing Genre – Visual Poetry

Visual poetry is arranging the words of a poem in a particular shape. The shape could be a symbol for the meaning of the poem.

Visual poems do not have a set structure. They allow you to use your own creativity and style. You can use words, phrases or sentences in your poem.

The sssneaky sssnake came sssslithering by

A Write your own visual poem about winter or Christmas time in the tree below.

Brainstorm some words and phrases to do with your idea. Use your senses. What can you see, touch, smell, hear and taste when you think about winter or Christmas time?

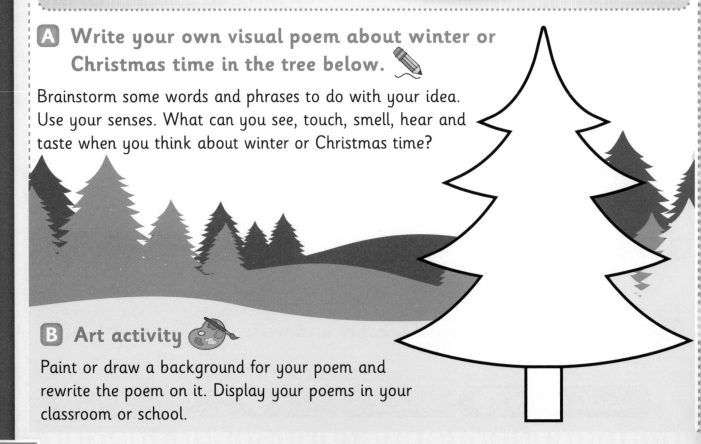

B Art activity

Paint or draw a background for your poem and rewrite the poem on it. Display your poems in your classroom or school.

Revision and Assessment

Revision: Grammar and Phonics

Look back at the grammar on pages 5, 11, 17, 23, 29, 35 and 41.

Day 1

1. **Ring the words that need a capital letter and add the missing punctuation.**

   (a) there was a beautiful butterfly in the garden announced orla

   (b) is that your laptop and case wondered kelly

2. **Write two examples of a noun.**

   (a) _____ (b) _____

3. **Underline the verb in these sentences.**

   (a) The fox captured its prey.

   (b) The teacher found a solution to the problem.

   (c) The mouse darted through the living room.

4. **Ring the correct adverb.**

   (a) I quickly / quackly moved the vase before my cousin knocked it.

   (b) She karelesly / carelessly tripped over my school bag.

5. **Write adjectives to enhance the following sentences.**

   (a) The student felt sick after eating the _____ cake.

   (b) The _____ girl tripped on a _____ step.

6. **Ring the correct spelling.**

   (a) antibiotic / entibiotic / antibyotic

   (b) entiwrinkle / antiwrinkle / antirinkle

   (c) antibackterial / entibacterial / antibacterial

Day 2

1. **Ring the words that need a capital letter and add the missing punctuation.**

   (a) where is rosie going on her school tour

   (b) look at the state of your bedroom declared mum

2. **Write two examples of a noun.**

   (a) _____ (b) _____

3. **Underline the verb in these sentences.**

   (a) The bird escaped from the cage.

   (b) The goblins stole the spells from the witches.

   (c) The door creaked open but there was nobody there.

4. **Ring the correct adverb.**

   (a) The toddlers played loudly / lowdly in the crèche.

   (b) The fox kawtiously / cautiously approached its prey.

5. **Write adjectives to enhance the following sentences.**

   (a) The _____ sisters were sent to bed.

   (b) It was a _____ day in the _____ resort.

6. **Ring the correct spelling.**

   (a) magesticelly / majestically / mejestically

   (b) robotically / robatically / roboticelly

   (c) kritically / critically / criticelly

Revision: Grammar and Phonics

Day 3

1. **Ring the speech marks and punctuation in these sentences.**

   (a) "I told him not to feed the lion but he wouldn't listen!" barked Kieran.

   (b) "The smell from the dump is turning my stomach," spluttered Breege.

2. **Write two examples of a noun.**

   (a) _____ (b) _____

3. **Insert a suitable adverb.**

   (a) The hungry boy ate his dinner _____ .

   (b) The gymnast balanced _____ on the beam.

4. **Write adjectives to enhance the following sentences.**

   (a) I won a _____ medal at the _____ contest.

   (b) The _____ librarian told a _____ story.

5. **Correct the punctuation in the following sentences.**

   (a) Donna asked me why I didn't want to go to the party

   (b) Are you coming now Colette asked Uncle Pat

   (c) You are hilarious giggled Destiny

6. **Ring the correct spelling.**

   (a) stench / stinch / stectch

   (b) krunch / cruntch / crunch

   (c) huntchback / hunkhback / hunchback

Day 4

1. **Ring the speech marks and punctuation in these sentences.**

   (a) "Do you know the way to the Strawberry Fields restaurant?" asked Ellie.

   (b) "I will never go to that dentist again!" said the boy with the swollen jaw.

2. **Write two examples of a noun.**

   (a) _____ (b) _____

3. **Insert a suitable adverb.**

   (a) The taxi driver drove _____ up the slippery hill.

   (b) The dog attacked the child _____ .

4. **Write adjectives to enhance the following sentences.**

   (a) The _____ bee buzzed around the _____ room.

   (b) The _____ boy cleaned his _____ bedroom.

5. **Correct the punctuation in the following sentences.**

   (a) Jude told Jasper to go away as he was feeling sorry for himself

   (b) Have you done your homework yet asked Mum

   (c) Did she actually let that snake slither around her asked Niamh

6. **Ring the correct spelling.**

   (a) vulture / future / vultur

   (b) capture / cepture / captur

   (c) pedicure / padicure / pedicur

Assessment: Phonics

A Ring the correct homophone.

1. My neighbour likes to die / dye her hair purple.
2. Please don't waste / waist the leftovers.
3. "I need more flower / flour for my cake," said Dad.
4. My pet hare / hair ran away.
5. Do you know where the male / mail toilets are please?
6. I need to right / write out my test again.

B Complete these sentences using a suitable '-anti' word.

1. There was a horrible taste from the _____ that the doctor prescribed.
2. The weather forecaster said there was an _____ coming from the west.
3. My grandmother uses _____ cream on her face.
4. Eddie washed his hands with _____ soap.
5. My brother uses an _____ spray before going for a run.
6. Denise turned the key in an _____ direction.

C Ring the correct '-nch' word to complete these sentences.

1. There was a stench / crunch when I bit into the apple.
2. There was a French / branch flag in our neighbour's garden.
3. Aideen sat on a bench / wrench with a cup of hot chocolate.
4. The sailor dropped the pinch / anchor overboard.
5. Mr scrunch / Lynch told me to run around the field two times.
6. I went to the munch / launch of a book in the Town Hall.

D Complete these sentences using a suitable '-or' word.

1. "Quick! Call the _____ . It's an emergency!"
2. Roald Dahl is the _____ of 'Matilda'.
3. The _____ came to visit our classroom to see what we were drawing.
4. " _____ , _____ on the wall, who is the fairest of them all?"
5. The ship sailed _____ during the _____ when it should have sailed south.
6. The student made an _____ in the test.

Assessment: Comprehension

A Christmas Carol

Scrooge had a very small fire, but the clerk's fire was so very much smaller that it looked like one coal. But he couldn't replenish it, for Scrooge kept the coal-box in his own room; and so surely as the clerk came in with the shovel, the master predicted that it would be necessary for them to part. Wherefore the clerk put on his white comforter, and tried to warm himself at the candle; in which effort, not being a man of a strong imagination, he failed.

"A merry Christmas, uncle! God save you!" cried a cheerful voice. It was the voice of Scrooge's nephew, who came upon him so quickly that this was the first intimation he had of his approach. "Bah!" said Scrooge, "Humbug!" He had so heated himself with rapid walking in the fog and frost, this nephew of Scrooge's, that he was all in a glow; his face was ruddy and handsome; his eyes sparkled, and his breath smoked again. "Christmas a humbug, uncle!" said Scrooge's nephew. "You don't mean that, I am sure." "I do," said Scrooge. "Merry Christmas! What right have you to be merry? What reason have you to be merry? You're poor enough." "Come, then," returned the nephew gaily. "What right have you to be dismal? What reason have you to be morose? You're rich enough." Scrooge having no better answer ready on the spur of the moment, said "Bah!" again; and followed it up with "Humbug."

"Don't be cross, uncle!" said the nephew. "What else can I be," returned the uncle, "when I live in such a world of fools as this? Merry Christmas! Out upon merry Christmas! What's Christmas time to you but a time for paying bills without money; a time for finding yourself a year older, but not an hour richer; a time for balancing your books and having every item in 'em through a round dozen of months presented dead against you? If I could work my will," said Scrooge indignantly, "every idiot who goes about with 'Merry Christmas' on his lips, should be boiled with his own pudding, and buried with a stake of holly through his heart. He should!"

"Uncle!" pleaded the nephew. "Nephew!" returned the uncle, sternly, "keep Christmas in your own way, and let me keep it in mine." "Keep it!" repeated Scrooge's nephew. "But you don't keep it." "Let me leave it alone, then," said Scrooge. "Much good may it do you! Much good it has ever done you!"

(From 'A Christmas Carol' by Charles Dickens)

Assessment: Comprehension and Vocabulary

A In your copy, go investigate.

1. Why was the clerk's fire much smaller than Scrooge's fire? Why could he not replenish it?

2. How did the clerk try to warm himself?

3. What was Scrooge's reply to his nephew when he said "A Merry Christmas, uncle"?

4. Why was Scrooge's nephew's face glowing?

5. What three reasons did Scrooge give as to why Christmas is not a happy time?

6. What did Scrooge say should happen to 'every idiot who goes about with "Merry Christmas" on his lips'?

7. Why do you think Scrooge is so unhappy and bitter?

8. What do you think other people think of Scrooge? Why?

`8`

B Vocabulary: Correct the following misspelled words from the text.

1. clirk		2. nefu	
3. replenash		4. balencing	
5. mastr		6. duzon	
7. candel		8. boyled	
9. crismas		10. sturnly	
11. hambug		12. pludding	

`12`

C Cloze procedure: 'Humbug!' Fill in the blanks.

window	locked	asleep	bed	Humbug	day	entered

Scrooge closed the _____, and examined the door by which the Ghost had

_____. It was double-locked, as he had _____ it with his own hands,

and the bolts were undisturbed. He tried to say "_____!" but stopped at the

first syllable. And being, from the emotion he had undergone, or the fatigues of the

_____, or his glimpse of the Invisible World, or the dull conversation of the Ghost,

or the lateness of the hour, much in need of repose; went straight to _____,

without undressing, and fell _____ upon the instant.

`7`

Assessment: Grammar

A Insert capital letters and full stops where necessary.

once upon a time there was a lovely, kind, imaginative girl called linda she lived in a little village called daisyville which was surrounded by meadows, wild flowers and rolling hills one day, linda decided to go on an adventure she brought her three best friends, roisín, laoise and aoibhinn with her they set off into the woods and they spent their time making a treasure trail, a hide-out and a bridge however, they soon began to feel hungry luckily, linda had remembered to bring a picnic there were cherry tarts, sausage rolls and lemonade for everyone afterwards, they decided it was time to go home as it would be getting dark soon they would definitely return to their magical place again

Capital Letters [17]   Full Stops [10]

B Ring the verbs in these sentences.

1. John bolted the new gate into the wall with a drill.

2. Sam planted colourful sections of flowers in the garden.

3. Grace and Mary baked a homemade apple tart and it smelled delicious.

4. Billy will leap for joy when he hears the great news.

5. Michael, Kieran and Sean are going on a boat trip and they will take their fishing rods.

[5]

C Write these nouns in the correct box.

clock   python   aunt   Florida   tiger   bike   South Pole
poodle   lollipop   France   firefighter   Kerry   principal   badger
television   parent   London   Mrs O'Keefe   laptop   lion

Person	Place	Thing	Animal

[20]

D Dictation: Listen to your teacher and write the sentences in your copy.

(I can do this!) (I'm getting there.) (I need help!)

Helen Keller Biography

9

Comprehension Strategies

A Before reading: Quick flick

Use the strategy of **Predicting**. Look at the key vocabulary below and predict what you think the story of Helen Keller will be about.

sick	blind	deaf	read	write	speak	college	inspire	famous

B During reading: Detective work

Use the strategy of **Determining Importance**. Fill in the table as you gain the information.

Who?	What?	Where?	When?	Why?

C During reading: I wonder …

Use the strategy of **Questioning**. Fill in the thought bubbles with questions about the text.

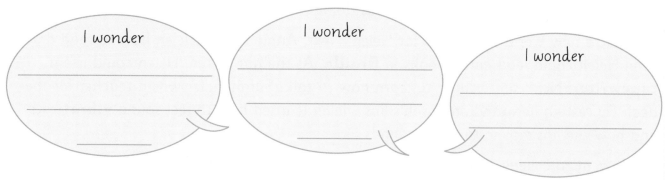

I wonder _____

I wonder _____

I wonder _____

D After reading: Use your senses

Use the strategy of **Visualising**. In pairs, create a sensory story book for a child who is visually impaired. Use the story 'We're Going on a Bear Hunt' as a stimulus. Use a variety of materials to tell the story, e.g. words cut out of sandpaper, braille, grass for the grass, bark for the trees in the forest, fur for the bear, etc. Use audio clips for sound effects or record yourself reciting the story.

Comprehension

 Use your dictionary to find out the meaning of the **bold** words below.

Helen Keller Biography

Helen Keller was born on 27 June 1880 in Alabama, USA. When she was a **toddler**, Helen became very sick. When Helen recovered, her parents soon realised that she had lost both her sight and her hearing. Helen found it **extremely** difficult to **communicate**.

Helen's parents found a woman named Annie Sullivan who had been blind, but had her eyesight **restored** by **surgery**. Annie came to work with Helen on 3 March 1887 and would be her helper and **companion** for the next 50 years. Annie began to teach Helen words. She would press the letters of words into Helen's hand. For example, she would put a doll in one of Helen's hands and then press the letters of the word D-O-L-L into the other hand. Helen would repeat the words into Annie's hand. However, Helen still didn't understand that the hand signs had meaning. Then, one day, Annie put Helen's hand into water coming from a **pump**. Then she spelled out W-A-T-E-R into Helen's other hand. Something **clicked**. Helen finally understood what Annie was doing.

An **entire** new world opened up for Helen. Next, Annie taught Helen how to read and soon Helen could read entire books in **Braille**. At the age of ten, Helen could use a **typewriter**. Next, she wanted to learn how to talk. Sarah Fuller was a teacher for the deaf. By resting her hand on Sarah's lips, Helen learned how to feel sound **vibrations** and how the lips moved to make sounds.

Helen went to college and began to write about her experiences of being deaf and blind. These were later **published** in a book called 'The Story of My Life'. As Helen grew older, she wanted to help other people like herself. She wanted to **inspire** them and give them hope. She travelled the country giving speeches and raising money. Later, during the Second World War, Helen visited **wounded** army soldiers **encouraging** them not to give up. She met many presidents of the USA and became friends with famous people such as the **inventor** of the telephone Alexander Graham Bell and the author Mark Twain. Helen died on 1 June 1968 at the age of 87.

A In your copy, go investigate.

1. Where and when was Helen Keller born?
2. What happened to Helen when she was a toddler?
3. Who did her parents find to help her?
4. How was Helen taught to learn words?
5. Name one of Helen's famous friends.

B In your copy, give your opinion.

1. How do you think it felt being blind and deaf?
2. Do you think Helen was a determined person? Why/Why not?
3. What would have happened if Annie had not come to work with Helen?
4. What happened when Annie put the water on Helen's hand and spelled out the word water?
5. Why did Helen want to inspire others?

C Vocabulary: Find words in the text to match these definitions.

1. Not in good health
2. A friend
3. Mother and father
4. Cannot see
5. A person who invents things
6. Injured

D Cloze procedure: 'Louis Braille'. Fill in the blanks.

Louis Braille was _____ near Paris in 1809. As a toddler he used to watch his _____ make shoes. One day, he _____ up a sharp pointed tool for making holes in leather called an awl. The awl slipped, piercing his _____ and damaging it beyond _____. The other eye became _____ and before long Louis was completely _____. Louis had learned about 'night writing' from soldiers who had used it to send messages at night during battles. Louis went on to develop a system for reading based upon a series of raised _____. The Braille system is now used worldwide.

Phonics – /ue/ sound family
'-ue', 'u_e', '-ui', '-ew', '-oo'

'**-ue**', '**u_e**', '**-ui**', '**-ew**' and '**-oo**' make a **long u** sound.

A Fill in the columns below using 'long u' words from the table.

school	spoon	bruise	duke	raccoon	news
shrewd	fruit	cruise	blew	new	two
renew	juice	noon	cube	brew	hue
moon	Tuesday	June	statue	argue	shampoo
rescue	clue	spoon	blue	glue	cute
fuel	duet	queue	tissue	stew	balloon

-ue	u_e	-ui	-ew	-oo

B Complete these sentences using a suitable 'long u' word from the table above.

1. I wish we had _____ at the weekends!

2. Eilish and Brian are going to sing a _____ on stage.

3. I have to _____ my zoo membership card.

4. Teresa and Anne are going on a Mediterranean _____ next summer.

5. Sinead has to buy some _____ before she can wash her hair.

C Say the 'long u' word. Fill in the missing letters and colour.

resc __ __	tiss __ __	shamp __ __	ball __ __ n
gl __ __ __	sp __ __ n	J __ n __	rac __ __ n
j __ __ ce	stat __ __ __	n __ __ s	st __ __
bl __ __ __	c __ t __	cl __ __ __	cr __ __ se

Colour Code

colour '-ue' words yellow
colour '-oo' words red
colour 'u_e' words blue
colour '-ew' words orange
colour '-ui' words green

Grammar – Pronouns

A **pronoun** is a word that takes the place of one or more nouns.

Example: Michelle's friends came to dinner. **She** gave **them** chicken and potatoes.

She and **they** are pronouns.

More pronouns – I, you, he, she, we, they, it, who, her

A Complete these sentences using a suitable pronoun.

1. Alma helped me with my project. _____ is so helpful.

2. Aidan loves popcorn. _____ ate the entire tub.

3. Callum and I were arguing. _____ have to sit apart now.

4. Charlie took Trixie for a walk. _____ had to drag _____ along as she was tired.

5. Stacy and Max saw a UFO last night. _____ were terrified.

6. Aideen has a beautiful coat. _____ is so stylish.

B Look at the underlined pronouns. Write the person or object that the pronoun stands for.

1. "<u>I</u> don't like that song," said Caoimhe to Cathal. _____

2. "Did <u>you</u> take the last biscuit?" Tom asked Grandad. _____

3. I love this programme. <u>It</u> makes me laugh. _____

4. Rachel heard a noise downstairs so <u>she</u> went to investigate. _____

5. Claire helped me to make lasagne. <u>She</u> is very good at cooking.

6. Ronan and Joe are great friends. <u>They</u> play together all the time. _____

C In your copy, write your own sentences using these pronouns.

our   you   us   my   him   we

D Dictation: Listen to your teacher and write the sentences in your copy.

I can do this!   I'm getting there.   I need help!

53

Oral Language

A Oral report

Choose a famous person from history, e.g. Neil Armstrong, Anne Frank, Albert Einstein. Research your famous person. Using your strategy of determining importance, choose some key points. Prepare a two-minute presentation for your class. Use prompt cards or pictures to help you.

Writing Genre – Report Writing

A **report** is a factual account. A **biography** is an account written about the life of a person.

When planning a report you can use **categories**. This will help to order your ideas into **paragraphs**. For biographies, categories can include:

- Where is the person from?
- What do they look like?
- What was their childhood like?
- Why are they famous?
- What inspired them?
- What is their legacy?

Also include a **title** and **concluding comment**.

> **Top tip!**
>
> When reading, it helps to use small sticky Post-its to mark the most important points. This will help you to summarise the text. A point is important if you can **justify** why it is important.

A Plan and draft a biography report on the famous person that you have researched. Use the questions below as a guide.

Where are they from?

What was their childhood like?

Why are they famous?

What inspired them?

What do they look like?

What is their legacy?

B Drama: Hot-seating

Imagine Helen Keller visited your classroom. What questions would you ask her? Make a list of questions and enact the scenario.

China – The Red Dragon 10

Comprehension Strategies

A Before reading: KWL chart

Use the strategies of **Making Connections** and **Questioning**. Use the chart below to record your background knowledge of China and anything you hope to find out from reading the text. Record what you have learned after reading.

KWL Chart		
What I know	**What I want to know**	**What I have learned**

B During reading: Text by subject

Use the strategy of **Determining Importance**. Categorise information from the text under the headings below.

People	Landscape	Animals	History

C After reading: Oral summary

Use the strategy of **Summarising**. In pairs, summarise the main points of the text. Present your summary orally to the class.

Comprehension

STOP! Use your dictionary to find out the meaning of the **bold** words below.

China – The Red Dragon

With a **population** of over 1.3 billion, China has more people than any other country on earth. About a third of the population live in cities, and the rest of the people live in the countryside. China has lots of different landscapes, including mountains, **plateaus**, deserts and forests. The tallest mountain on earth, **Mount Everest**, sits on the border between China and Nepal. China has thousands of rivers. The two main rivers are the **Yellow River** and the **Yangtze River**, which both flow from west to east.

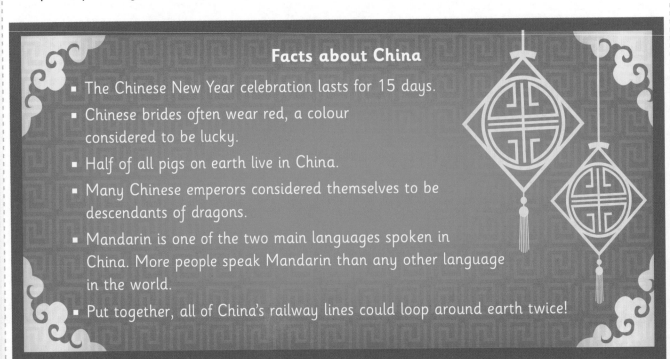

China is home to hundreds of **species** of animals and plants. More than 3,800 species of fish and hundreds of **amphibians** and **reptile** species live in the rivers, lakes and **coastal** waters. The **giant panda** lives in the misty mountains of central China and nowhere else on earth. The pandas can usually be found in thick **bamboo** forests, where they feast on the leaves. Due to **habitat** loss and hunting, these bears are on the **endangered** species list. It is estimated that only around 1,000 gaint pandas remain in the wild.

China is home to of one of the world's oldest **civilizations**. Ancient China was a land of invention. For centuries, China was much more **advanced** than most other countries in science and technology, astronomy and maths. The Chinese invented paper, the magnetic compass, printing, drinking tea, porcelain, silk and gunpowder.

Facts about China

- The Chinese New Year celebration lasts for 15 days.
- Chinese brides often wear red, a colour considered to be lucky.
- Half of all pigs on earth live in China.
- Many Chinese emperors considered themselves to be descendants of dragons.
- Mandarin is one of the two main languages spoken in China. More people speak Mandarin than any other language in the world.
- Put together, all of China's railway lines could loop around earth twice!

A In your copy, go investigate.

1. What is the population of China?
2. Name four types of landscapes found in China and name the two main rivers.
3. Where does the giant panda live and what do they eat?
4. What mountain is on the border of China and Nepal?
5. Name some inventions that come from China.

B In your copy, give your opinion.

1. Why do you think giant pandas are only found in China?
2. How have pandas become an endangered species? What can be done to protect them?
3. Why was Ancient China known as a land of invention?
4. Why do you think China has so many railways?
5. Write a list of things you would like to do if you were to visit China.

C Vocabulary: Chinese letters

Using the chart of Chinese letters below, write some of the words in bold from the text.

D Cloze procedure: 'Fantastic Facts'. Fill in the blanks.

The _____ New Year celebration lasts for 15 days. Chinese _____

often wear red, a colour considered to be _____ . Half of all _____

on earth live in China. Many Chinese emperors considered themselves to be descendants

of _____ . More people speak _____ than any other language

in the _____ . Put together, all of China's railways lines could loop around

_____ twice.

57

Phonics – Silent letters

Silent letters are letters that we do not pronounce when reading or saying words, e.g. sign. Silent letters are important for spelling and to help us tell the difference between some words.

Examples:

calf	autumn	wrench	knee	choir	tomb
chemist	hymn	knit	knock	scissors	listen
gnome	knew	wrist	Wednesday	gnash	muscle
plumb	wreck	limb	knuckle	gnaw	reign
knife	sword	anchor	rhyme	thumb	knight

A Say the words in the table. Pick a word from the table to write in each circle.

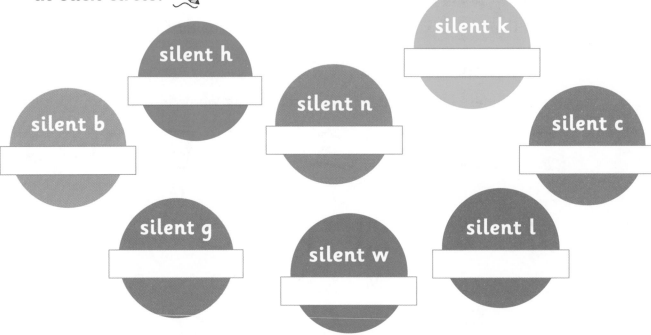

B Make a list of silent letter words that start with the following sounds.

kn			
gn			
wr			

C Underline the silent letters in the words below. In your copy, draw a picture or symbol to match each word.

comb	scratch	gnome	knuckle	white	gnaw
which	knitting	crumb	cheque	wrench	gnat

Grammar – Conjunctions

A **conjunction** is a joining word. We use conjunctions to join two words or phrases together to form one long sentence.

and and **but** are two of the most common conjunctions we use.

There are many other types of conjunctions that can be used to make your sentences more interesting.

Examples:

Time	Reason	Place	Condition
after	because	where	unless
before	therefore	wherever	in case
since	so that		provided that
whenever	in order		even if
while			

A Ring the conjunctions in these sentences. In your copy, say whether the conjunction is a time, reason, place or condition conjunction.

1. The doctor looked in my ears because they were sore.
2. I sold my Pokémon card in order to pay for the vase I broke.
3. I will not swim in the ocean in case I get swept out to sea.
4. I will buy two of the same dolls so that there will not be any bickering.
5. My dog barks whenever the doorbell rings.

B Use conjunctions from the table above to complete these sentences.

1. We couldn't go to the cinema _____ it was closed.
2. Take the steak off the heat _____ it has turned brown.
3. Odhran is very brave _____ Fionn is not.
4. Mason shared the last cake _____ Bobby could have some too.
5. Make sure you turn down the oven _____ it gets too hot.

C In your copy, write a sentence using each of the conjunctions in the table above correctly.

Example: I will go to the library **in case** Denise is waiting for me.

D Dictation: Listen to your teacher and write the sentences in your copy.

 I can do this!   I'm getting there.   I need help!

59

Oral Language

A Classifying objects

In groups, spend time sorting, pattern-making and grouping objects. Use maths or art materials. What makes the objects similar/different? Why do they go together?

As you work, use descriptive language to **(a)** describe what you must do, **(b)** describe what you are doing, **(c)** describe what you have done.

Writing Genre – Report Writing

The **language of reports** should include:

- reference to what/who it is about, e.g. Helen, the tutor, they
- timeless present tense – are, have, is, belongs, protects
- factual, precise adjectives – inspiring legacy, positive people

> **Top tip!**
> Do not include first-person pronouns (I, my, etc.) or opinions.

A Review, edit and rewrite your biography report. Include the language of reports shown above. You could also use some long sentences with conjunctions.

Check your work using the report self-assessment checklist. **P**

B Interview a relative or a person in your school. Create a list of factual questions. Write or record your interview and display it in the classroom.

Sample Interview Questions

- What is your happiest memory?
- Do you prefer being an adult or when you were a child? Why?
- What advice would you give me?
- If you could be any animal, which one would you be and why?
- What do you like to do for fun?
- Tell me about a funny time in your life.
- What was the nicest thing you ever did for someone?
- What do you think makes a good person?
- What is the best thing in the world?

Gorta – Self Help Africa 11

Comprehension Strategies

A Before reading: Crystal ball

Use the strategy of **Predicting**. Look at the title and image and use your crystal ball to predict what the text will be about.

I predict that…   I imagine that…      I wonder if…   I think that…

I think that … will be about, because…   Maybe… will be about, because…

B During reading: I wonder …

Use the strategy of **Questioning**. Fill in the thought bubbles with questions about the text.

I wonder _____

I wonder _____

I wonder _____

C During reading: What was that?

Use the strategy of **Clarifying**. We need to have something clarified when we read a word, a phrase or an idea that we don't understand. Is there anything in the text that you would like clarified?

D After reading: Fabulous five

Use the strategies of **Determining Importance** and **Summarising**. Record five key words from the text. Then, in groups, compare your 'fabulous five' and say why you thought these were the most important words.

Comprehension

 STOP! Use your dictionary to find out the meaning of the **bold** words and phrases below.

Gorta – Self Help Africa

Statement

'**Our vision is a rural Africa free from hunger and poverty.**'

Did you know that more than 250 million people in Africa suffer from hunger and **malnutrition**? They **struggle** every day in very poor conditions. Do you think that is fair? Would you switch places? Gorta – Self Help Africa is a charity that helps people run family-farms. They want to help these people and you can too! Here's why you should get involved.

gorta
Self Help Africa

Argument

The world's five most **unequal** countries are all in sub-Saharan Africa. The population is growing and the people are moving to towns in search of work. There is now even more pressure on farming as there are fewer people left to farm the land.

Sub-Saharan Africa is the area of Africa that lies south of the Sahara.

One in four people living in these areas is **undernourished**. Malnutrition is everywhere. It affects children's development and causes sickness and early death. Millions of under-fives die each year. Women and children are the worst affected by malnutrition.

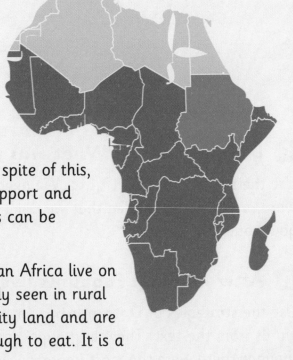

Women produce up to 70 per cent of the food grown on small farms in Africa. More than half of farmers in sub-Saharan Africa are women. In spite of this, African women receive just a **fraction** of the support and money available to men. As a result, their farms can be 20-40 per cent less **productive**.

More than 330 million people across sub-Saharan Africa live on less than $1.25 a day. Extreme poverty is mostly seen in rural areas. These people continue to work poor-quality land and are unable to sell at market. They grow barely enough to eat. It is a **never-ending cycle**.

Conclusion

So, what can you do to help I hear you ask? Fundraise.

Doing something in aid of Gorta – Self Help Africa will give you a great **sense of achievement** as every cent will help to make a dramatic difference to the lives of families in rural Africa.

Will you ignore the facts or will you make a difference?

A In your copy, go investigate.

1. How many people in Africa suffer from hunger and malnutrition?

2. What is Gorta – Self Help Africa? What do they do?

3. What causes the deaths of millions of under-fives?

4. What percentage of the food grown on small farms is produced by women?

5. Why are rural Africans so poor?

B In your copy, give your opinion.

1. Why do people move to the towns? Does this make things better?

2. Why are women treated unequally?

3. Why don't more men work on the land? What are they doing instead?

4. Why do you think people can't grow enough crops to eat?

5. Why does Gorta – Self Help Africa need our help?

C Vocabulary

In your copy, use the following phrases to summarise information from the text.

- Most people would agree that …
- The fact is that …
- A sensible idea would be to …
- Here are two reasons why …
- We all know that …
- It wouldn't be very difficult to …

D Cloze procedure: 'Making a Difference'. Fill in the blanks.

Gorta – Self Help Africa works in countries across sub-Saharan

_____ , tackling _____ and

improving the lives of local communities. The organisation works

Self Help Africa

both with its own African staff, and through local partners to do a range of programmes

in rural communities. Gorta – Self _____ Africa has _____ working on

agricultural and rural development projects in Uganda for more than 20 years. Ethiopia is

among the world's _____ countries. Up to 85 per cent of the population

depend on agriculture for _____ and livelihoods.

Phonics – '-el', '-al'

'-**el**' and '-**al**' make an **ul** sound at the end of words.

Examples:

camel	jewel	chapel	cathedral	crystal	capital
level	easel	kennel	festival	animal	hospital
angel	cancel	spaniel	nocturnal	plural	journal

A Arrange the words from the table above in alphabetical order.

1.	2.	3.
4.	5.	6.
7.	8.	9.
10.	11.	12.
13.	14.	15.
16.	17.	18.

B Tick the correct spelling of the '-el' and '-al' words below.

camel	hospital	journal	easel
camal	hospitel	journel	easal
angel	cathedral	kennel	spaniel
angal	cathedrel	kennal	spanial

C Complete these sentences using a suitable '-el' or '-al' word.

1. A _____ stores water in the humps on its back.

2. Brothers Grimm wrote the story of _____ and _____.

3. Bats and owls are _____ animals.

4. You will need an overnight bag for your stay in the _____.

5. There is a small _____ next to the _____.

Grammar – Changing statements to questions

A sentence that tells us something is a **statement**, e.g. My head was spinning from all the noise.

One way that a statement can be changed into a **question** is to use **do** – **does** (present tense), **did** (past tense) or **will** (future tense) as the first word.

Example: My sister enjoys playing camogie. (Statement)

Does my sister enjoy playing camogie? (Question)

A In your copy, make question sentences from the following statements using do, does, did or will.

1. Bakers make delicious desserts.
2. My sister works at the credit union.
3. He will spend a lot of time working in his office.
4. Avril will sing soprano in the choir.
5. James bought a new car last week.

B Change these questions into statements.

Example: Did Harry eat the last cake? Harry ate the last cake.

1. Does Paul take the dog for a walk every day?

2. Does Florence draw lovely pictures?

3. Did you break the vase?

4. Did the cat catch the mouse?

5. Will Rosie be at the school disco?

C What is happening in the comic strip? In your copy, write suitable statements and questions.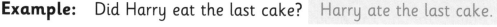

D Dictation: Listen to your teacher and write the sentences in your copy.

I can do this! 👍 ⬜   I'm getting there. ✋ ⬜   I need help! 👎 ⬜

Oral Language

A Argument circle

As a class, sit in a circle. Start with one pupil and move to the right. Each pupil must present a short argument 'for' the topic. Once everyone has spoken, move to the left and present an argument 'against' the topic. Use the topics below or think of your own.

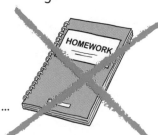

- We should not have a school dress code because …
- There should be no homework because …
- The school day should be shorter because …
- Children should be able to use mobile phones in school because …

Writing Genre – Persuasive Writing

The purpose of **persuasive writing** is to present an argument from a particular point of view. It may be written in the form of a debate, a letter or an advertisement.

Structure:

Statement – States the problem or argument. This is sometimes presented as a question.

Argument – Makes points arguing the position taken. The arguments 'for' are stated first, followed by the arguments 'against'.

Conclusion or summary – A summary of the main points or position.

A In your copy, plan and draft a persuasive piece about why homework should be banned. Use the guidelines below. Each argument should be presented in a different paragraph.

Statement: Homework should be banned.
Position taken: For/Against (choose one)
Argument for/against: Make your point. Elaborate on the point. Give evidence to back up your point.
Conclusion: Use a hook line or question to persuade the reader to go with your point of view.

B Drama: Class courtroom

Deirdre Murphy has been accused of stealing Bernadette Crowley's money that she fundraised for Gorta – Self Help Africa. Divide the class in two and act out the courtroom scene. One side is the defence and one side is for the prosecution. Teacher is the judge.

The Sugar Tax Debate

Comprehension Strategies

A Before reading: Figure it out!

Use the strategies of **Predicting** and **Inferring**. Look at the key words from the text below and predict what the article will be about.

diet-related disease	teeth extracted	processed food	food education	sugar addict	cheap

What will the article be about?

_____

Why do you think that?

_____

B During reading: Picture this!

Use the strategy of **Visualising**. Draw an image <u>for</u> the argument and an image <u>against</u> the argument. Why did you choose these images?

For	Against

C After reading: I wonder …

Use the strategy of **Questioning**. Do you still have questions about the text? Fill in the thought bubbles.

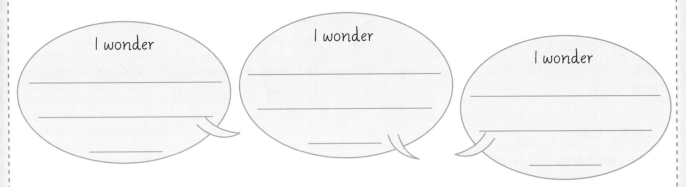

I wonder _____

I wonder _____

I wonder _____

Comprehension

 Use your dictionary to find out the meaning of the **bold** words below.

The Sugar Tax Debate

A sugar tax is when you pay extra money for a product because it contains sugar. It is a tool used by governments to try to get people to cut down on buying too many sugary things.

Statement
Should there be a tax on sugar?

Argument

For	Against
Sugar is responsible for health problems across the world.	It will be the public, not soft drinks companies, that will end up paying the costs of the new tax.
The amount of **processed** food and sugar-sweetened drinks that people are eating and drinking is frightening. Do you know what these foods contain?	The tax is badly **targeted**. Fruit juices and milk-based drinks will be excluded, meaning some of the most-sugary drinks will escape the tax. For example, a standard extra-large hot chocolate contains 15 teaspoons of sugar – double the **recommended** daily maximum for an adult. But because it's a milk-based drink, it will be exempt from the tax.
The amount of children having teeth **extracted** due to sugar **consumption** has increased dramatically.	
We need to go back to our roots and learn how to cook from scratch.	
The money raised from a sugar tax should be used for food education to prevent diet-related disease from continuing.	The tax will hit the poorest hardest – why should the rich get richer while the poor get poorer?
The Government needs to make it easier for people on lower **incomes** to have access to fresh fruit and vegetables.	The amount of people drinking soft drinks is actually falling. **Statistics** show that purchases of soft drinks have actually decreased.
Are you a sugar **addict**? Do you want to have a diet-related health condition? The change has to be made now, before it's too late.	It's only a bit of sugar, and it's cheap, so why not enjoy it?

Conclusion:

There should be a tax on sugar.

There should not be a tax on sugar.

A In your copy, go investigate.

1. What is a sugar tax?

2. What should the money from sugar tax be used for? Why?

3. Why do so many children need teeth extractions?

4. Why will the tax hit the poorest hardest?

5. What does the Government need to do for people who do not earn a lot of money?

B In your copy, give your opinion.

1. Why do you think this topic has been highlighted?

2. Why are people eating so many processed foods and drinking sugary drinks?

3. What effect will too much sugar have on your health in the future?

4. From which other source do you think people might get their sugar hit?

5. What should happen, in your opinion?

C Vocabulary: Categorising

Fill in the table below with words associated with **(a)** a sugar-filled diet, **(b)** a healthy diet.

Sugar-filled Diet	Healthy Diet

D Cloze procedure: 'The Story of Sugar'. Fill in the blanks.

Sugar cane has been grown for centuries in tropical _____. It is thought to

have _____ been used in the Polynesian Islands of the Pacific Ocean over

5,000 years ago. People used to _____ the raw sugar cane because it was so

_____. Later, sugar spread to other areas of the

world through trade. It arrived in Europe in the 16th century.

Until then, Europeans had used _____ to

sweeten food. _____ began to replace honey

and was known as 'honey without bees'.

Phonics – '-ant', '-ent'

'**-ant**' and '**-ent**' are suffixes. They sound like they are written.

dent	plant	bent	pant	tent	sent
accountant	consultant	went	servant	ant	urgent
agent	client	different	excellent	important	elegant
patient	tolerant	abundant	infant	cent	accident

A Write the correct '-ant' or '-ent' word from the table under each image.

B Complete these sentences using a suitable '-ant' or '-ent' word from the table.

1. My uncle went crazy when he saw the _____ in his car.

2. I began to _____ after walking up six flights of stairs.

3. The Garda said we had to come to the station as it was _____.

4. I had to return the dress as it was _____ to the one I had ordered.

5. The princess looked very _____ in her ballgown.

C Do you remember what an antonym is? (A word with the opposite meaning.) Write antonyms from the table for the following words and phrases.

master		few		on purpose	
straight		stayed		shabby	
adult		received		no rush	

Grammar – Exclamation mark

An **exclamation mark** is a punctuation mark used to show a range of emotions.

Examples:

To show anger – You hurt me!

To ask for help – Please help me!

To show joy – Those flowers are so lovely!

To show surprise or excitement – I can't believe that you came first!

Used after one word or after a short word – Oh! I'm so disappointed.

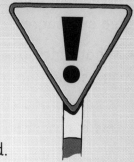

A Write words and phrases to show how this boy might feel on his birthday. Don't forget the exclamation marks!

B Insert a full stop, an exclamation mark or a question mark.

Will the performance be on TV	I am soaked to the bone	Is that a tarantula	I have a long list of chores
The car is covered in ice	I went to France in May	Who made the school rules	I'm exhausted

C Change the full stops to exclamation marks where necessary.

The alarm clock went off as normal. I sluggishly made my way downstairs. At first I thought my eyes were deceiving me. I rubbed them vigorously and looked again. Snow. There was a beautiful blanket of glistening white snow covering everything in sight. Fabulous. This was just what I wished for. I couldn't wait to get outside to build a snowman and make snow angels. No school for me today. This was going to be the best day ever.

D Dictation: Listen to your teacher and write the sentences in your copy.

I can do this! 　　I'm getting there. 　　I need help!

Oral Language

A Debate with your mate!

In pairs, make an argument for or against the following topics. Do you and your partner agree or disagree?

- What time do you usually go to bed at? Do you think you should go to bed earlier? Why/Why not?
- What do you eat for your breakfast? Do you think this is a healthy option? Why/Why not?
- What do you do when you get home from school? Are you tired? Why/Why not?
- How many hours of TV do you watch a day? Do you think this is too much? Why/Why not?

Writing Genre – Persuasive Writing

The **language of persuasion** should include:

- nouns and pronouns – the Government, the school
- the present tense – need, want
- technical terms – processed, tax
- no personal pronouns – 'everyone knows', 'each of us believes'

Use some of these words and phrases to enhance your persuasive writing.

Adding	Sequencing	Illustrating	Cause and Effect
and	first, second, third	for example	because
also	finally	such as	so
as well as	next	for instance	therefore
Comparing	Qualifying	Contrasting	Emphasising
similarly	but	whereas	above all
likewise	however	instead of	in particular
as with	although	alternatively	especially

A Review, edit and rewrite your persuasive piece about homework. Include the language features shown above.

Check your work using the persuasive self-assessment checklist.

B Art activity

Design a poster showing the position you took about homework in your persuasive piece.

The Life-cycle of a Butterfly

13

Comprehension Strategies

A Before reading: Describing butterflies

Use the strategy of **Visualising**. What words come to mind when you think of a butterfly? How would you describe it? Fill in the word wall using the headings below.

Shape	Size	Texture	Movement	Colour

B After reading: Learning new words

Use the strategy of **Word Attack**. Pick out three words from the text. Say which word attack strategy you used to figure them out.

Word _____
W.A.S. _____

Word _____
W.A.S. _____

Word _____
W.A.S. _____

C During reading: Key points

Use the strategy of **Determining Importance**. Record a key point from each stage of the life-cycle of the butterfly.

Stage 1	Stage 2	Stage 3	Stage 4

D After reading: Oral summary

Use the strategy of **Summarising**. In pairs, summarise the main points of the text. Present your summary orally to the class.

Comprehension

 STOP! Use your dictionary to find out the meaning of the **bold** words below.

The Life-cycle of a Butterfly

Definition: A butterfly is an insect.

Stage 1 – the egg

A butterfly starts its life as an egg. The female butterfly lays a cluster of eggs on leaves or **stems** of plants. Inside these tiny eggs, caterpillars grow. The eggs can be different shapes and textures. They can be oval, round or **cylindrical**, and bumpy, smooth, or wrinkled. The time it takes for the eggs to hatch changes with different **species**, some will **hatch** within a few weeks, others will only hatch once the weather is warm enough.

Stage 2 – the caterpillar

Once ready, the caterpillar (larva) **hatches** from its egg. It starts to eat immediately. First it eats the leaf it was born on and then continues to **munch** all the leaves around it. It begins to grow really quickly. As it grows, the caterpillar gets too big for its skin. It sheds its skin to make room for its bigger body. When the old skin comes off there is a new larger skin underneath.

Stage 3 – the pupa

Once fully grown, the caterpillar makes a pupa (or chrysalis). This covers the caterpillar and keeps it hidden. It also protects it from **predators** and **extreme** weather conditions. Inside the pupa the caterpillar starts to change into a butterfly (**metamorphosis**). This stage may last a few weeks or even months.

Stage 4 – the butterfly

Once the butterfly is ready to **emerge**, the case around the pupa splits open. At first, the wings are wet, soft and wrinkled against its body. The butterfly is also tired. It rests and waits for its wings to dry. While resting, it pumps blood into its wings to make them strong. After some practice, the butterfly takes to the air in search of flowers to feed on and other butterflies to mate with. The cycle is complete – and ready to start all over again!

Summary: A caterpillar transforms into a butterfly.

A In your copy, go investigate.

1. Outline the very first thing that happens in the cycle.
2. Describe the shapes and textures of the eggs.
3. What happens to the caterpillar's skin?
4. What protects the caterpillar from predators and extreme weather?
5. What does the butterfly have to do before it takes flight?

B In your copy, give your opinion. ❓

1. Why does the butterfly lay its eggs on leaves or stems of plants?
2. Why does the caterpillar eat its way out of the egg?
3. What would happen if the pupa was damaged?
4. Why do you think it takes some species longer to form?
5. Do you think a butterfly bonds with its parents? Why/Why not?

C Match one of these key words from the comprehension with a definition. ✏️

butterfly	when a caterpillar changes into a butterfly
eggs	when the butterfly comes out
caterpillar	what grows inside the egg
chrysalis	another name for a pupa
metamorphosis	a colourful insect
emerge	what a butterfly lays

D Cloze procedure: 'Amazing Butterflies'. Fill in the blanks. ✏️

Butterflies are amazing _____. There are almost 15,000 species of butterfly in the world. The life-cycle of the butterfly is made up of _____ ____ parts. Caterpillars eat _____ and grow bigger. They undergo changes to their _____ in a _____. When they are ready to _____ they have _____ into colourful butterflies. After some practice, the butterfly is able to _____ and goes in search of _____ to feed on. The cycle is ready to _____ again.

Phonics – '-pre'

'**-pre**' is a prefix. It comes at the beginning of a word.

Examples:

predict	prevent	prepare	premature	prefix
preview	premiere	preference	presumption	precaution
prescribe	premiership	prehistoric	president	prefer

A Match a '-pre' word from the table with a definition below.

1. To make a guess about something

2. To get things ready

3. The first showing of a film

4. When a doctor gives you medicine

5. Ensure something does not happen

B Tick the correct spelling of the '-pre' words below.

prepair		prefur		preview	
prepare		prefere		prefew	
preepare		prefer		prevewe	
prefent		pradict		premere	
prevent		predict		premiear	
prevint		predicte		premiere	

C Complete these sentences using a suitable '-pre' word from the table.

1. The _____ of Ireland lives in Áras an Uachtaráin.

2. I went to the Natural History Museum to view the _____ creatures.

3. I took my inhaler before the match as a _____.

4. You will need to _____ a lunch for the tour tomorrow.

5. The baby was born early. The baby was _____.

Grammar – Commas

A **comma** is a punctuation mark that tells the reader to pause during a sentence.

Example: Before we have dessert, you must eat all of your vegetables.

We also use commas to separate lists of actions.

Example: I like to play with Aoife, Sheola, Mae and Eabha.

Commas allow you to combine two ideas into a single sentence.

Example: While I finished my homework, my friend played the piano.

A Insert the three commas missing from this verse. Read the verse with and without commas. What is the difference?

> *May your thoughts be as glad as shamrocks*
>
> *May your heart be as light as a song*
>
> *May each day bring you bright happy hours*
>
> *That stay with you all the year long.*

B Ring the correct sentence.

Anne, Grace and Kaitlin went to a pool party.   Anne Grace, and Kaitlin went to a pool party.
May, June and July are the months of summer.   May June and July, are the months of summer.
France Italy Spain and Ireland are in Europe.   France, Italy, Spain and Ireland are in Europe.

C Write five sentences using commas.

1. _____

2. _____

3. _____

4. _____

5. _____

D Dictation: Listen to your teacher and write the sentences in your copy.

I can do this!   I'm getting there.   I need help!

Oral Language

A Show and tell

In pairs, choose an object (a toy, a game or a kitchen utensil) and prepare an oral explanation of how the object works.

Writing Genre – Explanation Writing

Explanation writing explains how things come to be the way they are, or how or why something happens.

Structure:
- **Title**
- **Definition** – what it is
- **Description** – how it works and interesting facts
- **Summary** – main points

A In your copy, plan and draft an explanation of the life-cycle of a frog. Use the guidelines below.

Title:	
Definition:	
Description/Stages:	
Summary:	

B Art activity

Draw a series of four images to explain the life-cycle of a frog.

1.	2.	3.	4.

Top tips to get you started!

1. Eggs laid in water **2.** Tadpoles swim and breathe in the water using gills **3.** Froglet – still has some of its tail but can breathe using lungs **4.** Frog-tail has been absorbed

All About Rainbows

Comprehension Strategies

A Before reading: Think ahead

Use the strategy of **Predicting**. How do you think a rainbow is formed?

_____

_____

B Before reading: Picture this!

Use the strategy of **Visualising**. Draw the image you imagine when you think of a rainbow.

C During reading: Fabulous five

Use the strategy of **Determining Importance**. While reading, record five key words in the text. Then, in groups, compare your 'fabulous five' and say why you thought these were the most important words.

D After reading: This reminds me of …

Use the strategy of **Making Connections**. While reading, stop along the way and make connections to:

- yourself – This reminds me of a time I …
- another text – This reminds me of something I read …
- the outside world – This reminds me of what I know about …

Comprehension

STOP! Use your dictionary to find out the meaning of the **bold** words below.

All About Rainbows

In 1666, a scientist called Isaac Newton discovered that if sunlight passed through a triangular piece of glass called a **prism**, the white light would **split** into a band of seven colours. This band of colours was made up of red, orange, yellow, green, blue, indigo and violet light. These are the colours of the rainbow in the order that they appear.

After it rains, the air in the **atmosphere** is filled with raindrops. Each raindrop acts like a tiny prism. If sunlight passes through raindrops at just the right angle, the light is split into an **arc** of colours with red on the outside of the arc and violet on the inside. So, rainbows happen when sunlight and rain join together. The **angle** for each colour of a rainbow is different, because the colours slow down at different speeds when they enter the raindrop. The light leaves the raindrop in one colour, depending on the angle it came in, so we see only one colour coming from each raindrop.

The most brilliant rainbow displays occur when part of the sky is still dark with rainclouds and the **viewer** is in a sunny spot facing the sun. This creates a very bright and **vivid** rainbow against the dark **background**. Sometimes it is possible to see a second arc or double rainbow. This is caused by a double **reflection** of sunlight inside the raindrops.

If you're hoping to find a pot of gold at the end of the rainbow, you may be disappointed to find out that there is no real end of the rainbow. This is because rainbows do not actually exist in a particular **location** in the sky. A rainbow's position depends on the location of the **observer** and the position of the sun.

A In your copy, go investigate.

1. Which famous scientist was mentioned in the text?
2. What colours does a white light split into?
3. Rainbows occur when two things combine. What are they?
4. When do the best rainbow displays happen?
5. What does a rainbow's position depend on?

B In your copy, give your opinion.

1. How do you think Newton discovered the colours of the rainbow?
2. Why is the angle for each colour of a rainbow different?
3. What do you think a double rainbow looks like? Draw one.
4. Why is there no real end to a rainbow?
5. Why do some people think that there is a pot of gold at the end of a rainbow?

C Vocabulary: True or False

	True	False
1. Nine colours make up white light.		
2. To view a rainbow you must turn your back to the sun.		
3. Light leaves a rainbow in seven colours.		
4. William Shakespeare discovered the colours of the rainbow.		
5. After it rains, the air in the atmosphere is filled with raindrops.		
6. The angle for each colour of a rainbow is the same.		
7. Sometimes it is possible to see a second arc or a double rainbow.		
8. Green is the colour on the outside of the arc.		
9. Violet is the colour on the inside of the arc.		
10. You will find a pot of gold at the end of a rainbow.		

D Cloze procedure: 'Rainbow Facts'. Fill in the blanks.

Rainbows are _____ of colours that can be seen in the _____.

Isaac Newton was a _____ who identified the _____

colours that make up white light. Rainbows occur after a _____ shower when

the _____ is shining. Irish _____ says that when you reach

the end of a rainbow you will find a pot of _____. The colours in a rainbow

are: red, _____, yellow, green, blue, _____ and violet.

Phonics – '-ve'

'**-ve**' makes a 'v' sound.

Examples:

groove	alive	curve	observe	revolve	dissolve
leave	twelve	involve	deserve	starve	stove
solve	nerve	evolve	chive	retrieve	Steve
eavesdrop	conserve	active	sleeve	hive	sieve

A Draw an image for each of these '-ve' words.

twelve	sleeve	sieve	stove
hive	dissolve	Steve	curve

B Ring the correct '-ve' words to complete these sentences.

1. I like to get my **groove / groof** on on the dance floor.

2. "You must **dissolve / desolf** the tablet in water," said Dr Barry.

3. Steve put the note up his **sleife / sleeve**.

4. "Turn off the lights to **conserve / consurf** energy," demanded Dad.

5. "Thomas J was stung when a **hive / hove** full of bees emerged," cried Veda.

C Complete these sentences using a suitable '-ve' word from the table.

1. The detective managed to _____ the crime.

2. The scientist set up the microscope to _____ the frogspawn.

3. My mother says you shouldn't _____ on people's conversations.

4. I had to _____ my homework from my dog's mouth!

5. Aoife really did _____ to win student of the week.

Grammar – Sentences, phrases and paragraphs

A **sentence** is a group of words that tells a complete thought.

Example: Moya is playing the clarinet in the orchestra.

A **phrase** is a group of words that does not tell a complete thought.

Example: 'the roses in the garden'

A **paragraph** is a group of sentences about one main idea.

A In your copy, write sentences using the following phrases.

spick and span	an axe to grind	a bite to eat
cat out of the bag	as easy as pie	beating around the bush

B Tick 'phrase' or 'sentence' for each of the following.

	Phrase	Sentence
1. as sweet as sugar		
2. Liam carved a bedside cabinet for his granddaughter.		
3. a chill in the air		
4. Betty bought a bit of butter, but the bit of butter Betty bought was bitter.		
5. Bluebells arise from where you roam and butterflies flutter by and follow you home.		

C Read the following paragraph. In your copy, compose a paragraph about yourself.

My name is J.P. Lynch but my friends call me Seán. I live in Cork on the north side of the city. I have two brothers and two sisters. Their names are Kieran, Michael, Mary and Grace. I am the second eldest in the family. My dad works in the army and my mother works as a seamstress. I enjoy cycling, fishing and reading. We go to a place called Lahard on our summer holidays. We stay in a caravan near the seaside. I love being outdoors and I like the smell of rain.

D Dictation: Listen to your teacher and write the sentences in your copy.

I can do this!   I'm getting there.   I need help!

Oral Language

A Cause and effect

Discuss the cause and effect of the following: a rainbow, rain; treasure, a map; a snowman, snow; a house, a key.

Writing Genre – Explanation Writing

The language of **cause and effect** is a feature in explanation writing. **Cause** is the reason why something happened. **Effect** is the result of what happened.

'If', 'because', 'then', 'so', 'as a consequence', 'since', are some of the words you can use for cause and effect.

The **language of an explanation** should include:

- **Time conjunctions** – first, then, following
- **Cause and effect conjunctions** – if, because, then, so, this results in
- **Action verbs** – changes, reflects, discovers
- **Present tense** – acts, leaves
- **Adjectives** – distinctive, tiny

A Review, edit and rewrite your explanation of the life-cycle of the frog. Include the language features shown above and your own labelled diagram.

Check your work using the explanation self-assessment checklist. P

B Art activity

Create your own 'Life-cycle of a Butterfly'. You will need: a paper plate, green and yellow paper, pine nuts, pasta shapes and a black marker.

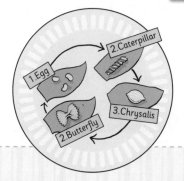

Abandoned Farmhouse 15

Comprehension Strategies

A Before reading: Impress with a guess!

Use the strategy of **Predicting**. In pairs, look at the title and illustrations and predict what the poem will be about.

'I think this poem will be about … because …'

_____

_____

Return to your prediction after you have read the poem.

B During reading: I wonder …

Use the strategy of **Questioning**. Fill in the thought bubbles with questions about the poem.

I wonder

_____

_____

I wonder

_____

_____

I wonder

_____

_____

C During reading: Reading between the lines …

Use the strategy of **Inferring**. What do you think the author is trying to tell us? Try to answer the 'I wonder' questions above. Use words like 'maybe', 'perhaps' or 'possibly'.

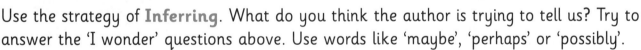

_____

_____

D After reading: Picture this!

Use the strategy of **Visualising**. Draw an image to show what you picture when you read the poem. Explain your drawing to your partner. Don't forget to use your senses.

Comprehension

 Use your dictionary to find out the meaning of the **bold** words below.

Abandoned Farmhouse

He was a big man, says the size of his shoes
on a pile of broken dishes by the house;
a tall man too, says the length of the bed
in an upstairs room; and a good, **God-fearing** man,
says the Bible with a broken back
on the floor below the window, dusty with sun;
but not a man for farming, say the fields
cluttered with **boulders** and the **leaky** barn.

A woman lived with him, says the bedroom wall
papered with **lilacs** and the kitchen shelves
covered with **oilcloth**, and they had a child,
says the sandbox made from a tractor tire.
Money was **scarce**, say the jars of plum **preserves**
and canned tomatoes sealed in the **cellar** hole.
And the winters cold, say the rags in the window frames.
It was lonely here, says the **narrow** country road.

Something went wrong, says the empty house
in the **weed-choked** yard. Stones in the fields
say he was not a farmer; the still-sealed jars
in the cellar say she left in a nervous **haste**.
And the child? Its toys are **strewn** in the yard
like branches after a storm—a rubber cow,
a **rusty** tractor with a broken **plow**,
a doll in **overalls**. Something went wrong, they say.

By Ted Kooser

A In your copy, go investigate.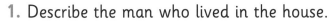

1. Describe the man who lived in the house.
2. What kind of things did the woman like?
3. What did the child play with?
4. What did they do to keep the cold out in winter?
5. What was left strewn in the yard?

B In your copy, give your opinion.

1. When do you think this poem is set? Why?
2. How do you know that the man was 'not a man for farming'?
3. What evidence shows that the family were poor?
4. What do you think happened to the family?
5. What do you think will happen to the farmhouse now?

C Vocabulary: Fill in the missing words from the poem.

He was a big man, says

on a pile of broken dishes by the house;

a tall man too, says

in an upstairs room; and a good, God-fearing man,

on the floor below the window, dusty with sun;

but not a man for farming, say the fields

cluttered with   .

D Cloze procedure: 'About the Poem'. Fill in the blanks.

The poem '   Farmhouse' is by an American poet called Ted

Kooser. The poem tells of a small   made up of a man, a woman and a

child, who live in a run-down   . They lead a simple life and do not have

much   . One day, something   happens. The family

have to evacuate the house in a   . The child's   are left

strewn all over the yard like   after a storm. This poem makes us feel a

sense of sadness. The poet uses   words such as 'broken' and 'lonely'. We

do not know what   of the family.

Phonics – '-gh', '-ough', '-augh'

'-**gh**', '-**ough**' and '-**augh**' can make the sound f or they can appear silent.

rough	cough	daughter	thought	caught	brought
laugh	naughty	draught	taught	fought	ghostly
yoghurt	distraught	enough	doughnut	Coughlan	drought
plough	gherkin	ghoul	dinghy	ought	bought

A Tick the correct spelling of each word and ring the '-gh', '-ough' or '-augh' sound.

cough	donut	gool	yogurt
cauff	doughnut	ghoul	yoghurt

dinghy	plough	thought	dauter
dinngy	plowe	thout	daughter

B Complete these sentences using a suitable '-gh', '-ough' or '-augh' word from the table.

1. The doctor thought I had a _____ .

2. The old lady was _____ when her dog died.

3. I went on a rubber _____ at the beach on my holidays.

4. The thief was _____ red-handed at the scene of the crime.

5. There was a _____ feeling at the haunted manor last night.

6. I really _____ to know the answer to this question.

C Ring the '-gh', '-ough' and '-augh' words in this paragraph.

Mr Coughlan owns a yoghurt company. It is thought he makes enough yoghurt for every person in Ireland! One day, his naughty daughter put a gherkin into one of the yoghurts! Mr Coughlan was mad. She was not allowed to eat her favourite doughnuts for a whole year. That taught her a lesson!

Grammar – Prepositions

A **preposition** is a word that helps us to add extra bits of information to sentences, e.g. The picture is **on** the wall. The horse jumped **over** the moon.

Examples

above	against	at	before	beneath
between	but	during	except	for
into	like	near	opposite	over
past	since	through	until	within

A Match the picture to the correct preposition and write the sentences in your copy.

beside the hat
in the hat
under the hat
on the hat
over the hat
behind the hat

B In your copy, use this table of phrases to write five sentences.

Example: The lady **in** the red **dress** was **near** the **door before lunch**.

Which one?	When?	Where?	Which direction?
description	time	location	location
in the red dress	before lunch	near the door	to the lake
with black tires	during the game	by the window	through the water
in high heels	at night	under the table	up the path
with blue dots	on Saturday	over the wall	across the bridge

C Dictation: Listen to your teacher and write the sentences in your copy.

| I can do this! | I'm getting there. | I need help! |

Oral Language

A **simile** is when you compare two things using the words **like** or **as**.

In the poem 'Abandoned Farmhouse', the author compares the toys strewn all over the yard to branches after a storm:

Its toys are strewn in the yard

like branches after a storm

Other similes:

as cool as a cucumber	as pale as a ghost	as sly as a fox
as white as snow	as timid as a rabbit	like two peas in a pod
eyes like a hawk	sings like an angel	as cold as ice

A Can you think of some other similes? Keep a record of them here and try to use them in your writing.

Writing Genre – Poetry Writing

Blank verse is a type of poetry that does not rhyme. It gives the poet the freedom of description without any rules. 'Abandoned Farmhouse' is an example of blank verse.

A Write your own poem about an abandoned mansion.

Plan your poem.

- Create a spider diagram and brainstorm the words you will use.
- Use adjectives from the list you made in Unit 5.
- Gather some of your favourite similes to try out.
- Plan your characters.
- Evoke your senses – what can you see, touch, smell, hear and taste?
- How will you create the mood?
- Will you use alliteration (when two or more nearby words have the same beginning sound)?
- How will you leave the reader guessing?

B Music: Add sound effects to your poem by using home-made instruments. What can you use to create a sense of atmosphere?

Fleming Discovers Penicillin

Comprehension Strategies

A Before reading: I wonder …

Use the strategy of **Questioning**. Fill in the thought bubbles with questions about the text.

I wonder ___

I wonder ___

I wonder ___

B During reading: Fabulous five

Use the strategy of **Determining Importance**. While reading, record five key words in the text. Then, in groups, compare your 'fabulous five' and say why you thought these were the most important words.

C During reading: This reminds me of …

Use the strategy of **Making Connections**. While reading, stop along the way to make connections to:

- yourself – This reminds me of a time I …
- another text – This reminds me of something I read …
- the outside world – This reminds me of what I know about …

This reminds me of …

D After reading: What was that?

Use the strategy of **Clarifying**. Why exactly was the discovery of penicillin so important?

_____

_____

Comprehension

— 29 September 1928 —

FLEMING DISCOVERS PENICILLIN

Alexander Fleming, a doctor from Scotland, has discovered a **revolutionary** treatment for infection. Through research and experimentation, Fleming has discovered a bacteria-destroying **mould** which he has called penicillin. Fleming believes his discovery will change the face of medicine as we know it. Penicillin will fight bacteria in your body and soon the killer chest infection could be a minor ailment! Many lives will be saved.

Alexander Fleming

During World War I, Fleming served in the Royal Army Medical Corps. He worked as a bacteriologist, studying wound infections in a makeshift lab. Through his research, Fleming discovered that commonly used **antiseptics** were doing more harm than good as the body is unable to break down harmful **bacteria**. More soldiers were dying from antiseptic treatment than from the **infections** they were trying to destroy. Fleming recommended that, for more effective healing, wounds simply be kept dry and clean. However, his recommendations largely went **unheeded**.

After returning from a family holiday this month, Fleming noticed that a **culture** of *Staphylococcus aureus* he had left out had become **contaminated** with a mould (now identified as *Penicillium notatum*). He noticed that the colonies of *staphylococci* surrounding this mould had been destroyed. When asked about his discovery, he said, "When I woke up just after dawn on 28 September, I certainly didn't plan to revolutionise all medicine by discovering the world's first antibiotic, or bacteria killer. But I suppose that was exactly what I did." At first, Fleming called the substance 'mould juice', but then named it 'penicillin' after the mould that produced it. The discovery is said to revolutionise the field of infection control.

A In your copy, go investigate.

1. Where was Alexander Fleming from?
2. What was his job during World War I?
3. What discovery did he make when he was working in the Royal Army Medical Corps?
4. What happened when Fleming returned from his family holiday?
5. How did his discovery help people?

B In your copy, give your opinion.

1. Why was Fleming's discovery so revolutionary?
2. What is a makeshift lab?
3. Why were so many soldiers dying?
4. Why did Fleming's recommendation about wound infection go unheeded?
5. Why did Fleming change the name from 'mould juice' to 'penicillin'?

C Vocabulary: Unscramble to find words from the text.

ingmleF	fectniinso	bioantitics	bla	covsidyer	cillepnin

D Cloze procedure: 'Bacteria are Everywhere!' Fill in the blanks.

Bacteria are tiny organisms which can live _____ – on and in bodies, in water; in the ground and on anything you can touch. You need a very powerful _____ to be able to see them. Bacteria can grow anywhere they can find the _____ they need. Most bacteria do not make you _____ but some can cause lots of illnesses when they get into a body: illnesses like ear _____, tonsillitis and food poisoning. If you get a cut and do not clean it, bacteria can make the place where you cut yourself _____, and can also spread to other parts of your body making you feel headachy, hot and sick, or even worse. Not all bacteria are _____. Some bacteria live inside our _____ and help to digest food and make vitamins like Vitamin K which helps to _____ against other harmful bacteria.

93

Phonics – '-ist'

'**-ist**' is a suffix. It is often used to describe a person who is practising something, e.g. pharmacist or novelist.

Examples:

artist	twist	insist	resist	canoeist	chemist
florist	soloist	specialist	harpist	scientist	guitarist
therapist	linguist	cyclist	psychologist	extremist	feminist
hypnotist	tourist	publicist	vocalist	motorist	dentist

A Tick the correct spelling of each word and ring the '-ist' sound.

florist	guitarised	focalist	canoeist
flowerist	gitarist	vocalist	canuist
florizt	guitarist	vokalist	kanoeist
florised	guitarast	vocaliste	canewist

B Draw an image to show what each of these people do.

hypnotist	motorist	artist	harpist

C Complete these sentences using a suitable '-ist' word from the table.

1. There is a special lane on some roads for a _____ to use.

2. When I was on holidays in Portugal, I was a _____ .

3. I had to go to a _____ to have my thyroid checked.

4. The _____ who sang at my cousin's wedding was fantastic.

5. I got two fillings when I went to visit the _____ .

Grammar – '-s', '-es', '-ies', '-ves' (singular and plural)

'**Singular**' means one. '**Plural**' means more than one. There are different rules for changing nouns from singular to plural.

For most words, just add an '**s**'.	cat → cat**s**
Words ending in a consonant and then '**y**': change the '**y**' to '**ies**'	sky → sk**ies**
Words ending in '**s**', '**x**', '**z**', '**sh**', '**ch**', '**ss**' or a consonant and then '**o**': add '**es**'	buzz → buzz**es**
Words ending in '**f**' or '**fe**': remove the '**f**' or '**fe**' and add '**ves**'	calf → cal**ves**
Some words are irregular and don't change at all.	sheep → sheep
Other words have a completely different spelling when plural.	foot → feet

A Change the words in brackets to their plural form.

1. There were two (dog)   playing in the garden last night.

2. In winter, the children have to wear (hat)   and (scarf)   .

3. The cow gave birth to three (calf)   altogether.

4. King Henry VIII of England had six (wife)   .

5. There are (peach)   and (cherry)   in the bowl.

Some nouns have a special plural form.

One	More than one	One	More than one
man	→ men	mouse	→ mice
woman	→ women	foot	→ feet
child	→ children	tooth	→ teeth

B Change the words in brackets to their plural form.

1. Both (child)   can swim.

2. I brush my (tooth)   every day.

3. Two (man)   stole the money.

C Dictation: Listen to your teacher and write the sentences in your copy.

 I can do this!   I'm getting there.   I need help!

95

Oral Language

A Tired words

In pairs or groups, discuss and make a class list of alternative words to use instead of 'then'.

Using your list, compose an oral story with the following story starter: *It was the middle of the night. Everyone else was asleep but Rosaleen was tossing and turning. Suddenly, she heard a noise. At that moment …*

Writing Genre – Recount Writing

Recount Writing tells about an event that happened in the past.
Who, **what**, **where**, **when** and **why** make up the main part of a recount.
We use linking words (first, next, then, afterwards, etc.) when writing about events that took place.

Structure:
- **Title**
- **Setting** – Set the scene. When and where did it happen? Who was there?
- **Event** – The events as they happened.
- **Concluding statement** – How did it end? What thoughts do you have about it?

A Plan and draft a newspaper article in the form of a recount about a news event from the recent past. Use the guidelines below.

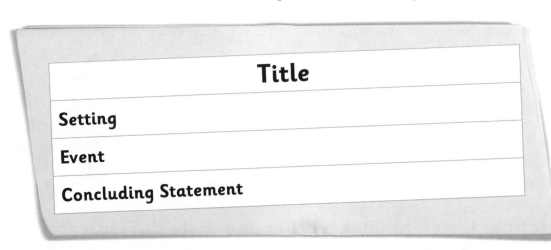

Title	
Setting	
Event	
Concluding Statement	

B P.E. Create a game that uses Who, What, Where, When, Why and How. For example, 'Sea, Ship, Shore'.

Stuck in Salou

Comprehension Strategies

A Before reading: Crystal ball

Use the strategy of **Predicting**. Look at the title and illustration and use your crystal ball to predict what will happen in the text.

I predict that…   I imagine that…   I wonder if…   I think that…

I think that … will happen, because…   Maybe… will happen, because…

B During reading: Key events

Use the strategy of **Determining Importance**. Name the key events that happened to the family in the order they occurred.

1st event	2nd event	3rd event	4th event	5th event	6th event

C After reading: Picture this!

Use the strategy of **Visualising**. Draw an image of the resort as you picture it.

Comprehension

 STOP! Use your dictionary to find out the meaning of the **bold** words and phrases below.

Stuck in Salou

Dear Auntie Mary,

Firstly, you will be glad to know that I am still alive, but only just! I am enduring the second week of the holiday from hell. According to the **brochure**, the resort in Salou was supposed to be a sunny, **sensuous**, sandy resort with ample activities for children and a supreme **state-of-the-art** swimming pool. Well, let me tell you about the events that have **unfolded** since our arrival.

To begin with, our flight was delayed by six hours. When we finally landed, we collected our luggage but noticed that Dad's suitcase was **drenched**. Orange juice had leaked all over his clothes (he has been wearing some of Mum's which has been a little bit funny). Next, we travelled by coach with freezing air conditioning to the **resort**, which explains my head cold. Upon check-in, we were led to our **secluded** apartment which smelled really **musty**. Just as I was about to hop into bed, the bed literally started hopping! Cockroaches! The place was **infested**.

The following morning, after a **fumigation** of our apartment, we decided to make the most of things and head to the pool. Loaded with our beach towels and blow-up beds, our smiles soon turned to frowns as we **encountered** a tiny pool covered in gooey green stuff! Could this holiday get any worse? Surely our luck was about to change! Nope – it started to rain!

Not just a little drizzle but a full-on **hurricane**! So we have been **confined** to our **atrocious** apartment for over a week now with tasteless food from the local supermercado and nothing but a deck of cards for entertainment. Mum says she hopes the cat is having a better time at home with you and that one thing is for sure, we will be staying at home next summer!

Looking forward (no really, really looking forward) to seeing you soon (3 days, 4 hours, 6 minutes and 40 seconds),

Love, your suffering niece, Nancy x

A In your copy, go investigate.

1. Where did Nancy go on holidays?
2. What were the first, second and third things that went wrong?
3. What happened when Nancy was about to jump into bed?
4. Why did the family's smiles turn to frowns?
5. How have the family been spending their holiday?

B In your copy, give your opinion.

1. Why is the holiday described as the 'holiday from hell'?
2. Did the brochure give a true or false account of the resort? Why?
3. What was the worst thing that happened to the family? Why?
4. Why did the apartment have to be fumigated?
5. Should the family complain? Why/Why not?

C Vocabulary: Find and record all of the time words or phrases in the passage.

_____

_____

_____

D Cloze procedure: 'Auntie Mary's Reply'. Fill in the blanks.

My dearest _____, I am so sorry to hear of your plight. What a terrible _____ you have been having. I hate to tell you, but we are enjoying a _____ wave here at home. The beaches have been thronged and the news reported that it is the best _____ we have had since the 1950s. Even the cat is lapping up the _____ of sunshine. We had the paddling pool in the garden yesterday and _____ a barbeque and ice-cream in the evening. I would say your cousins wish you were there to _____ with them but they are having so much fun they don't even notice you are gone. They are going to a waterpark _____ and to an amusement centre on Friday. Unfortunately, when you return on Saturday there is _____ forecast. Hope the last few days are bearable.

See you soon, Love _____ Mary

Phonics – '-inter'

'**-inter**' is a prefix. It means 'in the midst of', 'among' or 'between'.

Examples:

interval	interact	intersect	interlude	interpret
interactive	interview	intervene	internet	interfere
intercept	interweave	international	interested	interlinked

A Break these words into their prefix and root word. In your copy, write a sentence for each word.

	Prefix	Root		Prefix	Root
intercity			intermingle		
international			interlinked		
interchange			internet		
interview			interact		
interconnect			interweave		

B Match an '-inter' word from the table with a definition below.

1. A break in a theatre show

2. A meeting with employers about a job

3. To get involved in something you shouldn't

4. To be keen on doing something

5. A tool we use to search for information

C Complete these sentences using a suitable '-inter' word from the table.

1. My baby brother did not want to _____ with the other children.

2. The spy was asked to _____ a call from the agent.

3. In crochet you have to _____ patterns.

4. I am really _____ in learning about different countries.

5. There is a roundabout where the roads _____ .

Grammar – The apostrophe

The **apostrophe** is a punctuation mark that is used to show ownership, e.g. Lucy's rabbit.

The apostrophe can also be used to show that a letter or letters are missing, e.g. could not → couldn't. This is called a **contraction**.

A Rewrite these words as contractions.

1. we are

2. should not

3. she is

4. they would

5. it is

6. we will

7. does not

8. has not

9. will not

10. can not

B In your copy, rewrite these sentences adding apostrophes where necessary.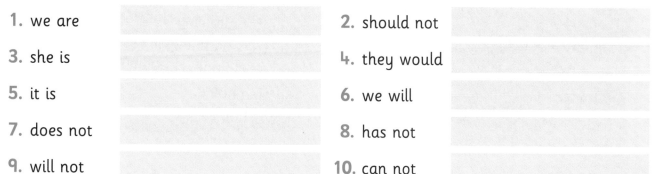

1. Peter doesnt want to share his cake with Toby.

2. Its a pity its raining as we wont be able to go on our picnic.

3. "Realtíns violin shouldnt be left on the sofa," barked Dad.

4. Fiachra hasnt got a ticket for the match on Sunday.

5. Mums car doesnt have enough petrol to get to school.

C Ring the correct spelling to complete these sentences.

1. Chris **won't** / **wo'nt** go out unless Emily comes too.

2. Kieran **does'nt** / **doesn't** want Deirdre to know that he has bought her a surprise.

3. "Paddy **shouldn't** / **should'nt** have eaten the entire swiss roll," cried Maria.

4. Fionn **has'nt** / **hasn't** found the spider yet, it **should'nt** / **shouldn't** take this long!

5. **We're** / **w'ere** a bit surprised that Elvira left the team.

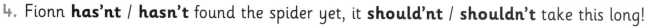

D Dictation: Listen to your teacher and write the sentences in your copy.

 I can do this!   I'm getting there.   I need help!

Oral Language

A Comparing and Contrasting

In pairs, discuss what is good or bad about the following recounts.

1.

Yo, how's it going? Did you hear we went on hols a while ago? It wasn't great. It was a bit of a dose. You wouldn't believe what happened. I won't be going there again anyway. Nightmare of a place. Anyway, see you some time, Joe

2.

Dear Samantha,
Our trip to Orlando didn't go quite as planned. Firstly, we missed our flight. Secondly, Dad lost his wallet. Following this, Mum broke her toe and finally my brother got the chickenpox. Looking forward to getting home.
Love, Louisa

Writing Genre – Recount Writing

The **language of a recount** should include:

- describing words, to give a clearer picture of what happened
- pronouns – I, we, he, they
- simple past tense – smelled, noticed
- action verbs – drenched, discovered
- linking time words – firstly, following

A Review, edit and rewrite your newspaper article. Include the language of recount listed above.

Check your work using the recount self-assessment checklist.

B Create a bank of words for your recounts.

Describing words	Action verbs	Time words

C Art activity

Design a brochure to advertise a family holiday destination. Include pictures and text and use lots of descriptive language.

Revision and Assessment

18

Revision: Grammar and Phonics

Look back at the grammar on pages 53, 59, 65, 71, 77, 83, 89, 95 and 101.

Day 1

1. **Ring the conjunctions.**

   (a) The optician looked into my eyes because they were stinging.

   (b) I sold my porcelain doll in order to pay for the antique I broke.

2. **Ring the word and symbol that make these question sentences.**

   (a) Does my mother-in-law make delicious chutneys?

   (b) Did your brother-in-law work in an insulating company?

3. **Say whether the following are sentences or phrases.**

   (a) as cool as a breeze

   Sentence ☐ Phrase ☐

   (b) Sam is very talented at playing the guitar.

   Sentence ☐ Phrase ☐

4. **Write a preposition to complete the sentence.**

   (a) Esme hid her treasures _____ the bed.

   (b) Dad left his keys _____ the car.

5. **Insert a question mark or an exclamation mark.**

   (a) Will there be a drama class on tomorrow

   (b) That is unbelievable

6. **Ring the correct spelling.**

   (a) skool / schul / school

   (b) bruise / bruze / brooze

   (c) resckue / rescue / rescew

Day 2

1. **Ring the conjunctions.**

   (a) I will not go in the paddle boat in case I get swept out to sea.

   (b) Joe wants to wear shorts _____ it is too cold.

2. **Ring the word and symbol that make these question sentences.**

   (a) Did Gary spend a lot of time in his shed?

   (b) Will Daniel go to work by bus?

3. **Say whether the following are sentences or phrases.**

   (a) as busy as a bee

   Sentence ☐ Phrase ☐

   (b) as tall as a giraffe

   Sentence ☐ Phrase ☐

4. **Write a preposition to complete the sentence.**

   (a) Rob and Saranne lived _____ Castle Troy.

   (b) The picture hung _____ the fireplace for 20 years.

5. **Insert a question mark or an exclamation mark.**

   (a) What a disaster

   (b) Can you give me directions to the GAA pitch please

6. **Ring the correct spelling.**

   (a) autumn / awtumn / autum

   (b) hym / hymn / hynm

   (c) noc / nok / knock

Revision: Grammar and Phonics

Day 3

1. **Change these words to their shortened form.**

   (a) we are _____

   (b) should not _____

   (c) she is _____

   (d) they would _____

2. **Write a conjunction to complete the sentence.**

   (a) We couldn't go to the marathon _____ it was cancelled.

   (b) Take the soup off the heat _____ it will boil over.

3. **Ring the word and symbol that make these question sentences.**

   (a) Will the children practise their spellings and tables every evening?

   (b) Do you like to play with Lego or do you prefer painting?

4. **Insert a comma in each sentence.**

   (a) Mum needs bananas kiwis and grapes for the fruit salad.

   (b) Shona ran jumped and tumbled in the gymnastics competition.

5. **Ring the phrase in each sentence.**

   (a) The water in the swimming pool was as cold as ice.

   (b) My brother walks as slow as a snail.

6. **Ring the correct spelling.**

   (a) kof / kough / cough

   (b) daughter / dawter / daughtr

   (c) tawt / taught / tawght

Day 4

1. **Change these words to their shortened form.**

   (a) it is _____

   (b) it will _____

   (c) does not _____

   (d) has not _____

2. **Write a conjunction to complete the sentence.**

   (a) Adam is very brave _____ Leo is not.

   (b) Ciara drank all the water _____ she was thirsty.

3. **Ring the word and symbol that make these question sentences.**

   (a) Does Jason have a baby brother or sister?

   (b) Do you want to go to the park or to the swimming pool?

4. **Insert a comma in each sentence.**

   (a) Paul's favourite dinners are pizza burgers and lasagna.

   (b) Naomi wrote a story with a beginning a middle and an end.

5. **Ring the phrase in each sentence.**

   (a) Cinderella cleaned until the house was spick and span.

   (b) Let's grab a bite to eat after the match.

6. **Ring the correct spelling.**

   (a) artest / artist / artisst

   (b) florist / floriwst / flerist

   (c) persist / percist / persist

Assessment: Phonics

A Say the word. Fill in the missing letters and colour.

fl__t__	resc__ __	barbeq__ __	d__ __
cr__ __se	stat__ __	f__m__	kangar__ __
ch__ __	br__ __se	ren__ __	igl__ __
fr__ __t	aven__ __	scr__ __	ch__ __se

Colour Code
colour '-ue' words yellow
colour '-oo' words red
colour 'u_e' words blue
colour '-ew' words orange
colour '-ui' words green

`16`

B Ring the silent letters in the following words.

castle	butcher	fasten
doubt	often	knife
lamb	honest	crumb

`9`

C Fill in the blanks using a suitable '-el' or '-al' word.

1. A _____ stores water in its hump.

2. The coach had to _____ the match due to the bad weather.

3. Would you prefer to wear flip flops or _____ going to the beach?

4. I sailed down the _____ in Amsterdam.

5. The _____ fell off my bike as I sped down the hill.

6. I keep my dog in a _____ in the garden at night.

7. Can you get the _____ so I can dig up the earth in the garden?

8. Sapphires and rubies are precious _____ .

`8`

D Ring the nonsense words.

prevent	prifent	prevent
prifer	prefer	prever
pretend	prietend	prentind
preedict	preydict	predict
presume	prezume	priesume
premere	premiear	premiere

`6`

Assessment: Comprehension

The Demon Headmaster

Dinah walked on round the playground, waiting for the bell to ring or the whistle to go.

But there was no bell. No whistle. Nothing. Instead, quite abruptly, all sounds in the playground stopped and the children turned round to stare at the school.

There on the steps stood a row of six children, three boys and three girls. They were all tall and heavily built and they were marked out from the others by a large white P sewn on to their blazer pockets. Without smiling, the tallest girl took a pace forwards.

'Form – lines!' she yelled into the silence. 'Yes, Rose,' all the children said, in perfect unison … Not quite sure what to do, Dinah stood by herself, a blotch of blue among the green.

The tallest boy on the steps walked forward. 'Lead-in!' he bellowed. 'Yes, Jeff,' chorused the children.

Still in total silence, they began to march forward, row by row, up the steps and through the door into the school, their eyes fixed straight ahead and their feet moving in step. There was no giggling or whispering or pushing …

Dinah continued to stand still, watching, until the playground was almost clear. As the last line marched off, she tacked herself on to the end of it and walked towards the school.

When she got to the top of the steps, Rose stuck out an arm, barring her way. 'Name?' she said briskly. 'Dinah Glass,' Dinah said. 'I'm new, and-' 'Just answer the questions,' Jeff interrupted her. 'What's that you're wearing?' 'It's my old school uniform. I-'

'Just answer the question,' he said again. There was no friendliness in his voice and as he spoke he looked not at Dinah but over her shoulder. 'It is not satisfactory. All pupils here shall wear correct green uniform. Kindly see to it.' He looked so haughty and spoke so stiffly that Dinah was irritated.

'I don't know why you're being so bossy,' she said coldly. 'Anyone'd think you were one of the teachers, instead of a measly kid like anyone else.' 'All pupils shall obey the prefects,' chanted Rose, in the same stiff voice. 'The prefects are the voice of the Headmaster.'

Dinah felt puzzled, but she was determined not to show it. She thrust her chin up and looked straight at them. 'Well, I think you should take me to see the Headmaster. I've got a letter for him.'

(From 'The Demon Headmaster' by Gillian Cross)

Assessment: Comprehension and Vocabulary

A In your copy, go investigate.

1. There was no bell and no whistle. What was there instead?
2. What did the children do when Rose yelled "Form – lines"? Why?
3. Why did Rose stop Dinah in the line?
4. How was Dinah spoken to by Rose and Jeff?
5. What did Dinah say to show she was irritated?
6. Why was Dinah puzzled? Why did she not want to show it?
7. What do you think the headmaster will be like?

7

B Vocabulary: Find words in the text that have the same meaning as the words listed below.

pleasantness		suddenly	
shouted		direct	
strolled		annoyed	
chime		grinning	

8

C Cloze procedure: 'The Demon Headmaster'. Fill in the blanks.

Dinah _____ on round the playground, waiting for the bell to ring or the whistle to go. But there was no bell. No _____. Nothing. Instead, quite abruptly, all sounds in the _____ stopped and the children turned round to stare at the school. There on the steps stood a row of _____ children, three boys and three girls. They were all _____ and heavily built and they were marked out from the others by a large white P sewn on to their blazer _____. Without smiling, the tallest girl took a pace forwards.

'Form – lines!' she _____ into the silence. 'Yes, Rose,' all the children said, in perfect _____ … Not quite sure what to do, Dinah stood by herself, a blotch of _____ among the green.

The tallest boy on the steps walked forward. 'Lead-in!' he _____.

'Yes, Jeff,' chorused the children.

10

107

Assessment: Grammar

A Use the conjunctions below to complete the sentences. ✏️

because   or   if   and   until

1. Paul was unemployed _____ he got a job.

2. Josie's estimate could be wrong _____ right.

3. Snakes _____ crocodiles are reptiles.

4. I went to bed _____ I was tired.

5. People couldn't watch television _____ the last century.

6. Elaine puts salt _____ pepper on everything.

7. I love to have fish _____ chips for tea.

8. I'll be disappointed _____ you can't come to the party.

8

B Use the prepositions below to write five sentences about this picture. ✏️

beside   under   on   next to   above

1. _____

2. _____

3. _____

4. _____

5. _____

5

C Dictation: Listen to your teacher and write the sentences in your copy. 👂

I can do this! 👍 ○   I'm getting there. ✊ ○   I need help! 👎 ○

Dictation

<u>Red</u> indicates phonics covered in the unit.

<u>Green</u> indicates grammar.

Purple indicates an additional activity or a question revising grammar taught recently.

Differentiation For weaker pupils, it is possible to shorten any of the dictation sentences.

Unit 1: Punctuation and '-anti'

1. <u>M</u>um wants some <u>antibacterial</u> soap and <u>antidandruff</u> shampoo from the shop.

2. <u>T</u>here is an <u>anti-smoking</u> and <u>anti-drug</u> policy in this building<u>.</u>

Unit 2: Nouns and '-ically'

1. <u>Siobhán</u> played the <u>drum</u> <u>rhythmically</u> in the concert.

2. <u>Historically</u>, the *Titanic* was known as the 'unsinkable <u>ship</u>'.

- Underline the nouns in each sentence.
- Why do the words Siobhán and *Titanic* have capital letters?
- Why do you think 'unsinkable ship' is in inverted commas?

Unit 3: Verbs and homophones

1. The <u>knight</u> gallop<u>ed</u> through the woods at <u>night</u>.

2. The <u>eight</u> players from the team <u>ate</u> an entire pizza each.

- Which tense are these sentences written in?
- Change each sentence to the present and future tenses.
- Which word has a silent k?

Unit 4: Adverbs and 'qu'

1. Sam <u>worriedly</u> watched the tiny <u>squirrel</u> stay <u>very</u> <u>quiet</u> during the <u>earthquake</u>.

2. Cian <u>carefully</u> read the <u>interesting</u> <u>quote</u> in the <u>Blue Planet</u> <u>aquarium</u> about the <u>equator</u>.

- Underline the adverbs.
- Write two other homophones for 'there'.
- Circle the capital letters and full stops.

Unit 5: Adjectives and '-nch'

1. The <u>lonely</u> <u>hunchback</u> spoke in a <u>husky</u> <u>French</u> accent.

2. There was a <u>broken brown</u> <u>branch</u> on the <u>wet</u> <u>bench</u>.

- Underline the adjectives.
- Which tense are these sentences written in?
- Where was the branch located?

Unit 6: Speech marks and '-ure'

1. "The bracelet is made of <u>pure</u> gold," said the jeweller.

2. "I went to the beauticians to have a <u>manicure</u>," smiled Emma.

- Circle the speech marks.
- Why does Emma have a capital E?
- Underline the nouns.

Unit 7: Verbs: Simple and continuous present and '-or'

1. <u>Taylor</u> was <u>talking</u> to the <u>doctor</u> this morning.

2. In <u>Portugal</u> the students have the <u>opportunity</u> to do <u>baking</u> and <u>swimming</u> at school.

- Underline the verbs in the continuous present.
- Why do Taylor and Portugal have capital letters?
- Write two homophones for the word 'to'.

Unit 8: Assessment

1. The <u>knight</u> gallop<u>ed</u> through the woods at <u>night</u>.

2. There was a <u>broken brown</u> <u>branch</u> on the <u>wet</u> <u>bench</u>.

- Write another homophone for the word 'through'.
- Underline the adjectives in sentence 2.
- Circle the capital letters and full stops.

Unit 9: Pronouns and /ue/ sound family

1. Did <u>you</u> see then length of the <u>queue</u> for the concert tickets?

2. <u>I</u> have to <u>renew</u> my zoo membership card.

- Circle the pronouns in each sentence.
- What is the name of the punctuation mark at the end of the first sentence and when is it used?
- Write a homophone for the word 'see'.

Unit 10: Conjunctions and silent letters

1. The <u>choir</u> sang a beautiful <u>hymn</u> <u>before and after</u> the service.

2. The <u>knight</u> took out his <u>sword</u> <u>while</u> he was riding his horse.

- Underline the conjunctions.
- Underline the word that shows the continuous present tense.
- Write a homophone for knight.

Unit 11: Statements to questions and '-el', '-al'

1. <u>Do</u> <u>camels</u> store water in the humps on their backs<u>?</u>
2. <u>Did</u> the Brothers Grimm write the story of <u>Hansel</u> and <u>Gretel?</u>

- Change these questions into statements.
- Underline the nouns.
- Circle the verbs.

Unit 12: Exclamation mark and '-ant', '-ent'

1. My uncle went crazy when he saw the <u>dent</u> in his car<u>!</u>
2. We <u>went</u> to the circus last weekend and it was amazing<u>!</u>

- Circle the exclamation marks.
- Which tense are these sentences written in?
- Underline the conjunctions in each sentence.

Unit 13: Commas and '-pre'

1. I <u>predict</u> that it will be rainy<u>,</u> windy and cloudy on Saturday.
2. There was a <u>preview</u> of the premiere in Waterford<u>,</u> Carlow and Westmeath.

- Circle the commas in each sentence.
- Explain why the following words have capital letters: Saturday, Waterford, Carlow, Westmeath.
- Change the second sentence to the present tense and future tense.

Unit 14: Sentences, phrases and paragraphs, and '-ve'

1. The detective managed to <u>solve</u> the crime quickly, there was no <u>beating around the bush</u>.
2. Mum cleaned the <u>stove</u> out and now it is <u>spick and span</u>.

- Highlight the phrase used in each sentence.
- Underline the pronoun used in the second sentence.
- Add adjectives to describe the following: detective, crime, stove.

Unit 15: Prepositions and '-gh', '-ough', '-augh'

1. I thought the <u>yoghurt</u> was <u>on</u> the table but it was actually <u>in</u> the fridge.
2. My <u>daughter</u> stood <u>in front of</u> her friend at the concert.

- Circle the prepositions.
- Underline the pronoun in the first sentence.
- Add an adjective to describe the following: yoghurt, table, fridge, daughter, friend, concert.

Unit 16: Singular and plural, and '-ist'

1. The **florist** put dais**ies** and ros**es** in the bouquet.

2. The **artist** used paint**s** and brush**es** to create his masterpiece.

- What is the singular of the following words: daisies, roses, paints, brushes?
- Break the following words up into their root word and suffix: artist, florist.
- Add in an adjective to describe the following: florist, bouquet, artist, daisies, roses, brushes, paints.

Unit 17: The apostrophe and '-inter'

1. Ciara's **interview** is on in the Principal's office on Tuesday.

2. The **internet** connection in Alison's house is worse than the one in Jack's.

- Circle the apostrophes.
- Explain why the following take an apostrophe: Ciara, Alison, Jack.
- Break up the words interview and internet into the prefix and root word.

Unit 18: Assessment

1. The **knight** took out his **sword** **while** he was riding his horse.

2. My **daughter** stood **in front of** her friend at the concert.

- Circle the prepositions.
- Underline the pronoun in the first sentence.
- Add an adjective to describe the following: knight, sword, horse, daughter, concert.

Cloze Procedure Answers

Unit 6

1. three
2. powers
3. woman
4. shirt
5. fire
6. escaped
7. poor
8. treasures
9. people
10. Tatra
11. starving

Unit 7

1. Paris
2. caricatures
3. oil
4. outdoors
5. Impressionists
6. *Poppy Field*
7. *Impression, Sunrise*
8. died

Unit 9

1. born
2. father
3. picked
4. eye
5. repair
6. infected
7. blind
8. dots

Unit 10

1. Chinese
2. brides
3. lucky
4. pigs
5. dragons
6. Mandarin
7. world
8. earth

Unit 11

1. Africa
2. poverty
3. Help
4. been
5. poorest
6. food

Unit 12

1. countries
2. first
3. chew
4. sweet
5. honey
6. Sugar

Unit 13

1. insects
2. four
3. leaves
4. bodies
5. pupa
6. emerge
7. changed
8. fly
9. flowers
10. start

Unit 14

1. arcs
2. sky
3. scientist
4. seven
5. rain
6. sun
7. tradition
8. gold
9. orange
10. indigo

Unit 15

1. Abandoned
2. family
3. farmhouse
4. money
5. terrible
6. hurry
7. toys
8. branches
9. sad
10. became

Unit 16

1. anywhere
2. microscope
3. food
4. sick
5. infections
6. sore
7. bad
8. bodies
9. fight

Unit 17

1. Nancy
2. time
3. heat
4. summer
5. rays
6. had
7. play
8. tomorrow
9. rain
10. Auntie

Unit 18

1. walked
2. whistle
3. playground
4. six
5. tall
6. pockets
7. yelled
8. unison
9. blue
10. bellowed